Starting Points for Vocabulary

P9-CDW-956

stuvwxyjseaohsdseoshpjacket
jitsevutjebghiozteewsopuswencz
jeansyzewsopuswencz
jeansywxzklmittenasleblouse
bootsurgpajamasleblouse

by Cheryl L. Callighan
illustrated by Philip Chalk

This book is dedicated to the memory of my father.
He taught me the joy of learning, the excitement of travel,
and the meaning of the word *loquacious*.

Publisher: Roberta Suid
Design & Production: Scott McMorrow
Cover Design: David Hale
Cover Art: Marilynn Barr

Other books in this series include:
*Starting Points for Language Arts, Starting Points for Reading, Starting Points
for Grammar,* and *Starting Points for Spelling.*

Entire contents copyright © 2000 by Monday Morning Books, Inc.,
Box 1680, Palo Alto, California 94302
For a complete catalog, write to the address above.

Call our toll-free number: 1-800-255-6049
E-mail us at: MMBooks@aol.com
Visit our Web site:
http://www.mondaymorningbooks.com

Monday Morning is a registered trademark of
Monday Morning Books, Inc.

Permission is hereby granted to reproduce
student materials in this book for non-commercial
individual or classroom use.

ISBN 1-57612-125-9
Printed in the United States of America
9 8 7 6 5 4 3 2 1

CONTENTS

INTRODUCTION

. . . .

Word study is important for a child's development. We often assume that children know the names of all the objects around them, yet this is not always the case. Students may have observed the large, round, brightly colored object in the classroom, but they are unable to identify it as a globe. Children may know that warm air comes from a place in the wall, but are unaware that the place is called a heat duct or register. Teachers must take time to carefully explain or label the names of items that are part of the child's world.

Teaching in the elementary grades involves much more than just the "three R's." In order to learn to read and write well, students need a broad experiential background. Ideally, these experiences should include travel, arts, crafts, music, cooking, household tasks, outdoor activities, exploration of nature, and plenty of exposure to books. Through these experiences a vocabulary is built. The greater a student's vocabulary, the more success he or she will have in reading, speaking, and writing endeavors.

In many of today's families, the hectic lifestyle does not allow time for parents to provide broad experiential and vocabulary-building activities for their children. The elementary teacher is therefore called upon to take up the slack. Many opportunities for vocabulary improvement are available in the classroom. For example, the simple project of making applesauce together provides students with vocabulary words such as mash, mix, stir, apple, peel, chop, sugar, cinnamon, and applesauce. These words may be used later in writing and spelling assignments. Such projects also enable students to practice cooperation and communication skills and develop them in groups. All of this work is important in building both oral and reading vocabularies.

Activities in the classroom become the foundation for ever-improving academic skills. Almost every project in the elementary grades can provide vocabulary-building opportunities. A walk outdoors can be the basis for using words about nature. A story about the zoo can lead to a lengthy list of animal names to be used later in both language arts and science activities. The importance of the use of adjectives and adverbs can be illustrated through looking at photographs and great works of art. Close examination of a caterpillar may lead to a student's first experience with writing accurate, descriptive sentences. And don't forget the "art" in Language Arts. Crafts and art projects may be used to introduce a lesson, culminate the learning of a particular concept, or provide a colorful means of communication for a reluctant writer. Each project will yield its own list of specific vocabulary words to be introduced or reinforced.

Bear

The purpose of this book is to expand and enrich vocabulary. It is not based on any required sight word or vocabulary list. Since these lists vary greatly among states and individual districts, a universally comprehensive list would be difficult to compile. Instead, this book draws its lists from subjects that might easily be the focus of children's writing, or those that are of high interest to children. The book is set up using a unit concept. A set of words is provided that correlates with each subject. Experiential and academic activities for each of these units are then based on the vocabulary words. The lists are designed to increase verbal as well as written vocabulary.

If you are constrained by district-mandated lists, you may adapt some of these activities to include the required words. The units are meant to be viewed as a menu. Pick and choose those activities that are suitable to your students' ages and abilities, and use them as a springboard to launch additional ideas of your own. Several units provide enrichment for other areas of the curriculum. The weather unit, for example, is an excellent companion to a similar science unit. The color unit is the perfect mate for a grammar unit on adjectives. Be sure never to view vocabulary as an isolated subject. Always bear in mind that every moment that you teach provides a golden opportunity to improve children's vocabulary.

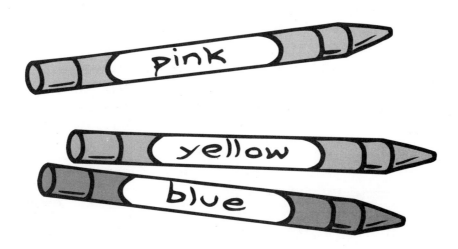

A Writing Philosophy

Children need to learn that writing is a means of communication. It involves putting ideas onto paper. Writers need to begin by thinking about what they want to communicate to the reader. Next they must find the exact words to most clearly state their ideas. Finally, writers must correctly arrange their words on paper so that they can be read and understood.

Here is an exercise to help children understand this concept. Hold a large writing tablet and seat the class around you. Tell the class to pretend that you have been given a monetary gift. The class must decide how to spend the money. Brainstorm ideas with the children. Write down all of their ideas, which might include toys, a pizza party, a submarine, books, candy, etc. Let the children know that these are all fun ideas, but that they are rather general and that you are not sure exactly what each child had in mind. Encourage the author of each idea to become more specific. Then put some of the more reasonable ideas into complete sentences and write them down on the tablet: "We need new playground balls for recess"; "Let's get books about animals for the reading center"; "I think we should have a pizza party if everyone is good all week." This exercise allows children to see how their ideas can be directly written in words.

Starting Points for Vocabulary © 2000 Monday Morning Books, Inc.

Children need to write about their own life experiences and ideas. They are very egocentric; their interest is greatest when a subject involves them personally. It is important to remember that a child's environment directly relates to his experience. A youngster could not write about an experience in a snowstorm if he or she lives in a climate where it never snows. Encourage children to start writing about simple every-day experiences such as a trip to the park, a very sad time, a funny event involving a pet, a family story, or an occurrence that was shared by the entire class.

As children become more confident in their writing, branch out into areas that will spark their imagination. Keep up with some of the latest books and movies that interest them. Use common childhood fantasies to help spark their writers' imaginations. Castles, dinosaurs, superpowers, and magical adventures never seem to go out of style.

It's important to remember that vocabulary is only one aspect of good writing. Writing requires a variety of skills that each child needs to master. Students need to acquire the mechanics of writing, such as understanding punctuation, capitalization, complete sentences, grammar, spelling, and paragraph form. (See *Starting Points for Grammar* and *Starting Points for Spelling* for help with many of these concepts.) They also need to understand how to organize information, follow a story line, and proofread. Creativity is also needed for writing. Topic choice, character development, and word selection can be handled in various creative ways by the author. Obviously, when teaching proper punctuation, creativity should not be encouraged. However, when you focus on the flow of ideas, let the students' imagination take flight.

Children need to write for many different purposes. Therefore the teaching of vocabulary cannot be an isolated subject. Students need a chance to write in a science journal, create posters or signs, translate personal feelings into words in a diary, develop skits with other group members, write both business and personal letters, develop stories, and write non-fiction reports. Allow students to write in subject areas that interest them most. Even a reluctant writer can develop organizational skills by producing a chart that lists ball players and their statistics. Just as you expose your class to a wide variety of reading genres, do the same in your writing activities.

Using This Book

• •

The contents of this book are presented in units. In each unit a list of vocabulary words is given that corresponds to a subject or theme. Suggested activities and projects that will develop the students' use of the new words follow each list. There are art projects, writing assignments, experiential activities, and reproducible worksheets.

Each vocabulary list contains 11 to 20 words. Use these words as a starting point: you may decide to work with only a portion of any given list or want to add several words of your own. Adapt the lists to suit the needs of your students and the requirements of your district.

The units are meant to be viewed as a menu of possibilities. Select those projects that you feel are best suited to your classroom. Many of the vocabulary activities can be used to cross over into other skill lessons. Additional word study concepts can also be found throughout the units. These include spelling, vowel sounds, syllables, synonyms, grammar, etc. By incorporating the various concepts, you will be able to provide a wide range of word study for your class. The building of a broad base of vocabulary will help your elementary students progress in their reading, writing, and communication abilities.

In addition to the vocabulary units, you will find a section on classroom environment. This includes a set of bulletin boards that can be used to highlight the concepts you are teaching. Several additional suggestions are included to help get the most out of your available classroom space.

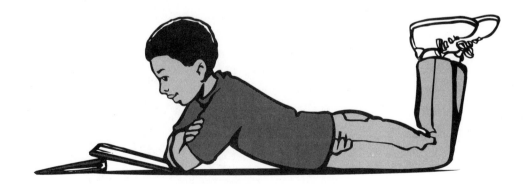

Puppy Power

· ·

Elementary students enjoy learning about the power of words. Even young children know that one or two words can evoke a strong image. This idea can be illustrated through a simple lesson.

Write this sentence on the board:

• I walked into my room and saw a dog.

Say: *This is a very general statement. It doesn't give us a clear picture. We don't know anything about the kind of dog. We don't have a good idea about what is happening.*

Write this sentence on the board:

• I walked into my room and saw a guard dog growling.

Ask: *How does this make you feel? Can you imagine what kind of story this might be about? What do you think this dog looks like?*

Write this sentence:

• I walked into my room and saw a roly-poly puppy on my bed.

Ask: *How does this make you feel? How is it different from the other sentences? What kind of story might this be about? Say: The words "roly-poly puppy" have a lot of power. They let you think about something special. Your writing can have Puppy Power, too. By carefully choosing your words, you can help your readers get a wonderful picture in their mind.*

Starting Points for Vocabulary © 2000 Monday Morning Books, Inc.

Puppy Power can become a buzz word in your classroom, meaning very descriptive writing or writing that evokes a particular emotion. You can use it to praise a student's efforts at writing: "Your story contained champion Puppy Power." It can also be used to help a student improve an assignment: "This section needs greater Puppy Power. Tell me more about what is happening."

As children learn more about the power of words, they will be more confident in their writing. By providing vocabulary-enriching activities in your classroom, you will be able to improve students' communication skills. This book will help you towards achieving that goal.

Classroom Environment

The elementary classroom should provide a positive environment for all students. Children at this age usually enjoy a lot of color around them. Pictures, artwork, student work, and posters can all be assets to your classroom and encourage an active environment. However, be careful that you do not overload the room with too much stimuli. It is better to frequently change displays rather than cover every available inch of space. Try to organize and cluster visual aids in your room. For example, one wall or bulletin board could be devoted to student work. Another area could be used to enhance a learning center. The space surrounding the chalkboard might provide space for the alphabet, the class schedule, and room helper charts. Reserve another bulletin board or wall area for educational displays regarding current subject matter or vocabulary development. Use the classroom space to teach and involve the students.

Learning centers are vital in the elementary classroom. Ideally a center contains table space and vertical display space behind it. Unfortunately, not many teachers are granted the ideal space. If this is true for you, you can use some of the wonderful storage containers that are available at the local discount store. Instructions for activities may be attached to the lids and supplies kept neatly inside. The lids may even serve as work surfaces when the center is in use. Large cardboard boxes may also be used as an activity station. Directions may be written on the sides and supplies kept inside. To save space, you can stack boxes with the opening toward the front. If you are handy with a sewing machine, consider creating a center from cloth. Use a large piece of denim for the background. Sew on various-size pockets of colorful material for storing direction cards, supplies, and even completed projects. Sew a header on the top and add a dowel rod to hang the center against a wall or suspend it from the ceiling to act as a room divider.

Children certainly enjoy utilizing floor space. Reading corners with comfy pillows and carpet squares are a great asset to any classroom. If bookshelves are unavailable, consider stacking colorful milk crates to house some books. A larger open area is wonderful for whole class activities. Children of this age also enjoy the concept of tents. Sheets or blankets may be draped over several desks under which the children may curl up to read or work in groups.

Your school's outdoor area can be another great educational spot. The play surface may be turned into a giant chalkboard. New textures and colors may be explored by sitting in the grass or examining a pile of leaves. If it snows in your part of the country, the schoolyard after a snowstorm may become a giant canvas for artists. Be creative as you look for new ways to provide experiences for your young students. The greater their experiential background, the more children's vocabulary will flourish and grow.

Bulletin Boards

Many teachers greatly dislike having to deal with bulletin boards. Yet, a bulletin board can be a powerful teaching tool. With some careful planning those large, blank expanses can become learning centers and valuable display areas. The subject of vocabulary lends itself very well to bulletin board instruction.

The concept behind the following bulletin boards is that you do the majority of the work just once. You create a background, or template, which is then updated throughout the year to keep the display current. Student participation may be incorporated to promote further learning.

Word Bird

Cover the board with light blue paper. Use cut-out letters to spell the title "Word Bird." Cut a long, thin strip of brown paper to represent a branch and staple it to the bottom of the display. Add several smaller branches and green leaves if desired. Cut a simple bird shape from red, blue, or yellow paper. Place the bird on the branch at the far left side of the bulletin board. Cut old brown grocery bags into strips. Crumple and twist the strips, then staple them on the branch in groups to create an empty bird's nest. Your background is now complete.

Starting Points for Vocabulary © 2000 Monday Morning Books, Inc.

Option I: Cut small bird shapes from brightly colored paper. Write a Pets vocabulary word (see p. 38) on each bird. Arrange the birds in the empty nest and staple them in place.

Option II: Cut one egg shape from paper in each of the colors listed in the Colors vocabulary list (see p. 27). Write the corresponding color on each egg. Let children look through magazines to find items that match each color. Glue these to the eggs. Staple the eggs in the nest.

Option III: Show the children the words from the Bugs vocabulary list (see p. 73). Let each child choose a bug. Give the children colored paper, scissors, glue, and markers. Have each child create a bug and label it with their vocabulary word. Arrange the bugs in the nest and staple them in place.

Option IV: Cut out feather shapes from brightly colored paper. Write a vocabulary word on each feather and place it in the nest.

Option V: Cut leaves from green paper. Add a vocabulary word to each leaf and staple the leaves around the nest. You could also add a branch to the top of the display to provide room for more leaves.

Starting Points for Vocabulary © 2000 Monday Morning Books, Inc.

Take a Closer Look

Cover the background of the bulletin board with white or light colored paper. Take two large pieces of black paper and roll each into a large cylinder. Tape the seams. You are going to staple the cylinders about three inches apart in the upper left corner of the bulletin board and staple a black square between the two cylinders to create a giant pair of binoculars. You may wish to add details such as a focus button on the rectangle and foil or plastic wrap in the cylinder ends to represent the lenses. Before you staple down the binoculars, draw a pair of eyes and a nose behind them. Use cut-out letters or a computer-generated banner to create the title "Take a Closer Look At:" The background is now complete.

Option I: Use cut-out paper squares, rectangles, and triangles to create simple buildings. Write a vocabulary word from the Our Town list (see p. 88) on each shape. Add the words "Our Town" after the colon in the title.

Option II: Have children cut out pictures of clothing items from catalogs. Label each item using the correct word from the Clothing vocabulary list (see p. 63). Add the word "Clothing" after the colon in the board title.

Option III: Use heart shapes to list emotions.

Option IV: Cut out book shapes and place a word from a specific story on each.

Option V: Use pairs of pear shapes to list homophone sets.

TAKE A CLOSER LOOK AT

TAKE A CLOSER LOOK AT

Our Town

museum

school

factory

houses

bank

library

hospital

stores

TAKE A CLOSER LOOK AT

loving

happy

Emotions

sad

grumpy

calm

worried

angry

surprised

shy

Starting Points for Vocabulary © 2000 Monday Morning Books, Inc.

A Mountain

Cover the background with light blue paper. Cut out a large, uneven triangle from brown paper to form the mountain. Add a triangle of white paper to the top for a snowcap. Use cut-out letters or a computer-generated banner to spell the title "A Mountain of Words." The background is now complete.

Option I: Cut out simple evergreen trees from green paper. Write a word from the Storybook People list (see p. 113) on each tree. Arrange the trees on the mountain and staple them in place. You may wish to add a few more details, such as a castle and a dragon.

Option II: Cut out rock shapes from gray and brown paper. Write one homophone on each gray rock and its matching word on a brown rock. Arrange the rocks in pairs around the mountain and staple them in place.

Option III: Add several free-form areas of white paper to the mountain to represent snow. Let each child design and create a snowman from paper. Have the students write any current list of vocabulary words on their snowmen. Place the snowmen on the mountain and staple in place.

Option IV: Add more snow to the mountain as described above. Draw a simple skier shape at the top of the mountain. Cut triangles from colored paper. Attach each triangle to a chenille stem (pipe cleaner) to create a set of pennants. Write a vocabulary word on each flag. Arrange them to represent a slalom course on the mountain and staple them in place.

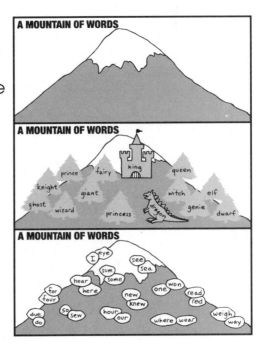

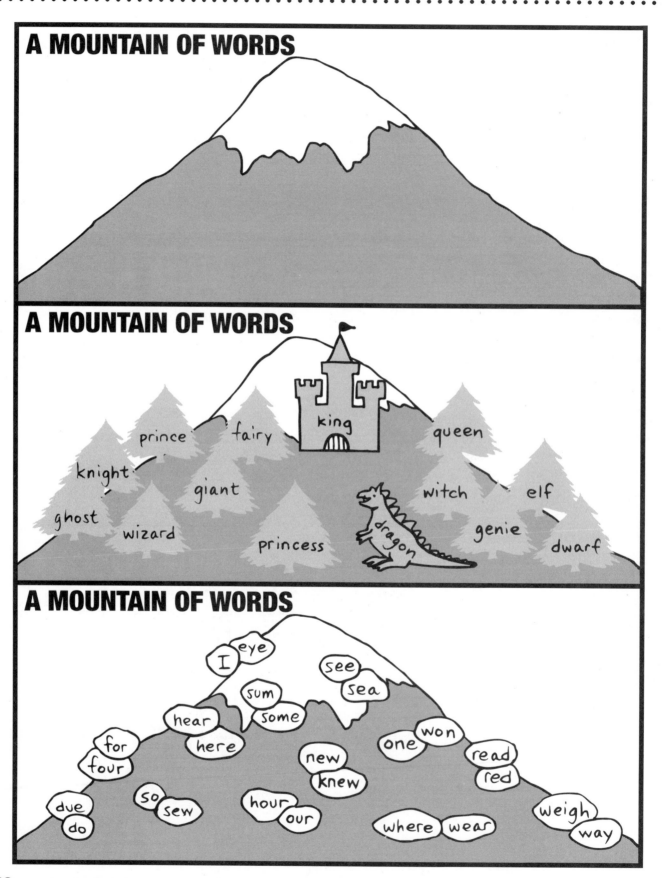

Starting Points for Vocabulary © 2000 Monday Morning Books, Inc.

The Puppy

Cover the background with a bright color. Use cut-out letters or a computer-generated banner to spell out the title "Add Puppy Power to Your Writing" (see p. 12 for more about Puppy Power). On the left-hand side place a puppy. Ready-made designs are available at most teacher stores or you can create your own by using an opaque projector to enlarge the drawing in this book. Your background is now complete.

Option I: Cut big and little circles from bright colored paper to represent toy balls. Write an appropriate word from the Size list on p. 81 on each circle. Add the balls to the display.

Option II: Let each student create a shoe from colored paper. Have the children write a vocabulary word, or an entire vocabulary list, on each shoe. Add the shoes to the display.

Option III: Write vocabulary words, perhaps the names of body parts, on white bone shapes and add them to the display.

Option IV: Cut out more puppy shapes. Write an animal word on each and add the puppies to the display. If desired, the puppies could be shaped to represent various adjectives, such as fat, thin, spotted, sleepy, etc. The children could determine an appropriate adjective for each puppy and label accordingly.

Add Puppy POWER To Your Writing

Add Puppy POWER To Your Writing

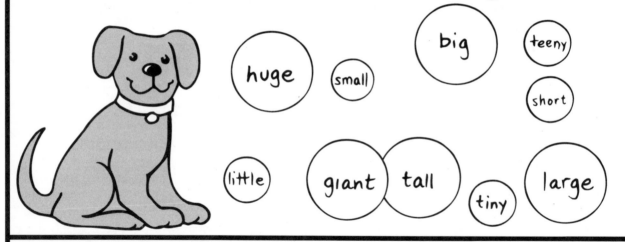

huge small big teeny short little giant tall tiny large

Add Puppy POWER To Your Writing

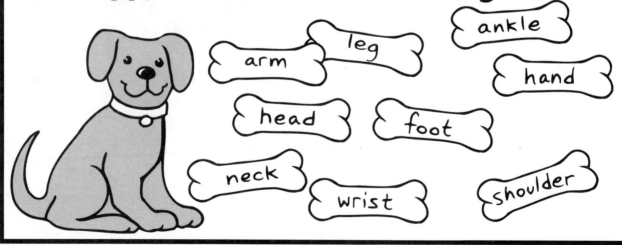

arm leg ankle hand head foot neck wrist shoulder

Starting Points for Vocabulary © 2000 Monday Morning Books, Inc.

The Sky

Cover the board with light blue paper. Use cut-out letters or a banner to spell out the title "The Sky's the Limit!" Arrange the title at the top of the display. Cut out two elongated triangles from brown paper. Place these at the very bottom of the display to represent rooftops. Add a red rectangle to each roof for a chimney. Use green paper for making wavy shapes that will represent treetops. Add these to the bottom of the bulletin board. Your template is now complete.

Option I: Cut out large clouds from white and gray paper. Write the title "Weather Words" on one cloud. Write the vocabulary words from the Weather list (see p. 54) on the other clouds. Place the clouds in groups on the display.

Option II: Cut out diamond shapes from colored paper to represent kites. Add some yarn or string to the bottom of each one. On one kite write the title "Contractions." Write a contraction (see p. 44) on each kite. Be sure to point out that the word "Sky's" in the title is a contraction.

Option III: Near Halloween, cut black bat shapes from paper. Use white correction fluid to write a vocabulary word on each bat. These words may be spooky words, Halloween terms, or any other set of vocabulary words.

Option IV: Use any of the following shapes for listing vocabulary words on this display: birds, airplanes, helium balloons, or hot air balloons.

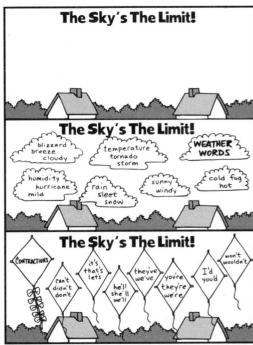

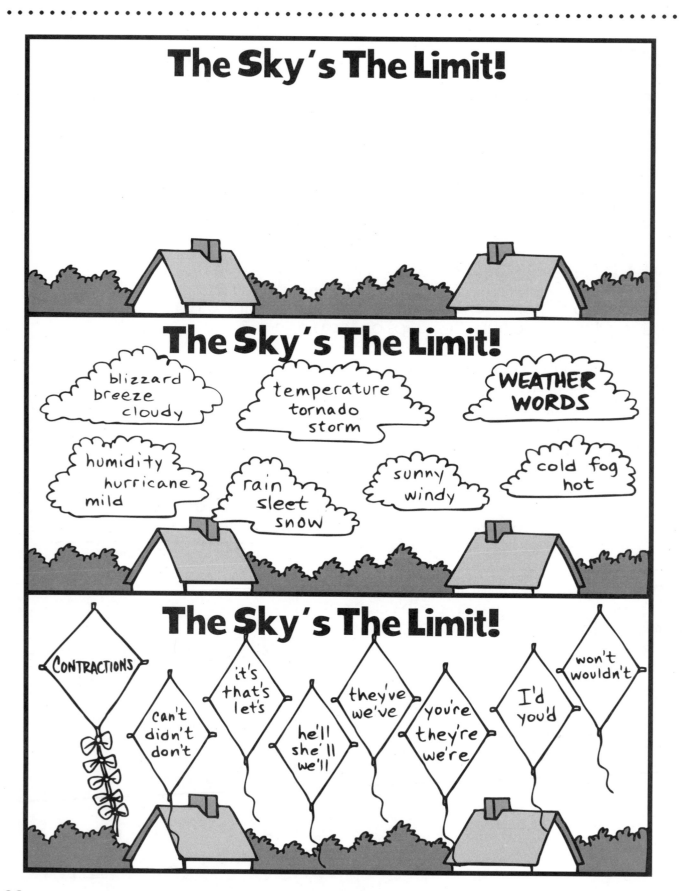

Starting Points for Vocabulary © 2000 Monday Morning Books, Inc.

Colors

Vocabulary List

black	blue	brown	green
orange	purple	red	white
yellow	pink	gray	

Activities:

1. Color Collages—Students classify colors, then practice speaking vocabulary words by describing objects on the collages.
2. I Hate . . . —A creative writing project with a little twist.
3. Color Mind Stretchers—Students use vocabulary words in an oral exercise based on divergent thinking skills.
4. Favorite Color Books—A classic project that combines organizational skills and creative writing.
5. ROY G. BV—A poetry project.

Word Study Extensions:

Colorful Spelling—Students use matching colors to write the words for a spelling lesson.
Adding Color—Writing sentences using the vocabulary words as adjectives.

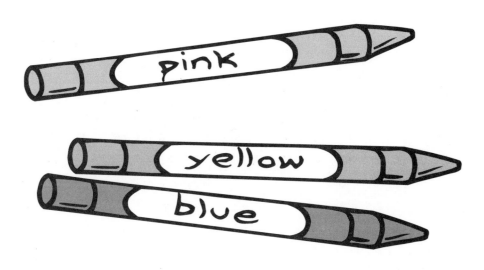

Color Collages

Purpose:
Students will relate vocabulary words to pictures and classify objects according to their color.

Materials:
Magazines, scissors, glue, poster board or large pieces of plain newsprint

Preparation:
1. Label each poster board or piece of newsprint with a color word. You may want to begin using only three colors.
2. Place the color posters on flat surfaces around the room. Place the magazines at a central location that is easily accessible to the children.

Procedure:
1. Show the class the posters. Let students read each color word on the posters.
2. Explain to the class that they are going to search through magazines to find pictures of objects that match the colors on the posters. When the students find a picture of an object, they should cut it out (the object only) and glue it to its matching poster. Let students continue working until the posters are filled.

Extensions:
1. To develop oral vocabularies, have one student describe an object on a poster. Let the class try to guess which item the student is describing. The child who guesses correctly may take a turn at describing a different object.
2. Ask students to find an object on a poster that starts with a particular letter or contains a specific vowel sound.
3. Use the posters as story starters. Ask students to write a story using as many pictured items as possible.

Starting Points for Vocabulary © 2000 Monday Morning Books, Inc.

I Hate . . .

Purpose:
Students will use a color word in a creative writing endeavor.

Materials:
Writing paper, drawing paper, pencils, crayons or markers

Procedure:
1. Spend some time talking with the students about colors that they do NOT like. This may be the color of a game marker that they never want to be stuck with. It could be the color of a cup that they have to drink from when no other cup is available. Maybe it is the color of an article of clothing that they hate to wear. After this discussion, have students think of several other things that they do not like that come in that same color.

2. After the discussion, give students an example of the writing assignment. Here is one sample:

> I hate red because of:
> > blood
> > sunburn
> > loud fire engines
> > radishes
> > cough syrup

3. Have the students choose their color and complete the writing assignment. Then have them draw illustrations to go along with what they have written.

4. You may want to let students add a line at the end of their list that tells about one thing that they DO like that has the color they have chosen.

> Example: I hate red, but I love cherry lollipops!

Color Mind Stretchers

Purpose:
Students will use vocabulary words in an oral exercise that promotes divergent thinking.

Procedure:
1. You don't need a scheduled time for this activity. You can ask a few of the mind stretchers while students wait in line at the end of the day, early in the morning before attendance is taken, to refocus the class after a hectic activity, or just before a story is read.
2. Tell the class that there is no right or wrong answer to these questions. The answers are all a matter of opinion, preference, and students' own feelings. Discuss with the children how all the answers will be correct, so no one should be teased because of what they say.

Here are some sample mind stretchers:

What color were the dinosaurs?
Name at least six colors that the sky can be.
What color are birds?
What color is summer?
What color is a smile?
What color is winter?
What colors make you think of your family? Why?
Name three colors for apples.
What color is autumn?
Which color best describes you? Why?
What color is spring?
Which color makes you feel happy? Why?
When are bananas not yellow?
What color is a whale?
Which color car goes the fastest? Why?
Which color is anger?
Which color makes you feel sad? Why?
When is having no color a good thing?
Name something that contains lots of colors.
What color would you like to paint your room? Why?
What color is there the most of in the world?
How many colors in the sun?

Starting Points for Vocabulary © 2000 Monday Morning Books, Inc.

Favorite Color Books

Purpose:
In this creative writing project, students will incorporate organization, classification, and writing in complete sentences.

Materials:
Colored paper, writing paper (preferably story paper with a blank area for a picture above and lines for writing below) or drawing paper, stapler, crayons or markers, magazines, scissors, glue

Preparation:
1. You will need two pieces of colored paper for each child.
2. Cut the story or writing paper into rectangles. You will need at least five pieces per child.

Procedure:
1. Tell students that they are going to think about their favorite color. They may have more than one favorite, but for this project they will need to pick just one.
2. Explain to the class that they are going to be creating books that tell about their favorite color. Each page of the book will have a picture and a sentence that tells about the picture. The books should be at least five pages long. Students may decide whether or not they want to cut out pictures from magazines or draw their own. Tell the class that there should be at least two of each type of picture in their books.
3. Spend a little time reviewing complete sentences with the class. Write several samples on the board. Take time to point out that a sentence begins with a capital letter and ends with a period. Tell the students that each sentence they write will describe or tell about their picture.

4. Give each child the five pieces of story or writing paper. Let students spend time cutting pictures from magazines or drawing their own illustrations. Remind the students that the pictures must contain their chosen color. This may be all that you want to complete in one day. The next step may take place at another class period.

5. Once all the pictures have been completed, hold a conference with each child. Have the students tell you the sentence that they plan to write under each picture. Let the students write the sentences. Be sure to have a second conference to check sentences and help students correct them.

6. After the children's pages are complete, give each child two pieces of colored paper that match their chosen color. These will become the front and back of their books. Tell students to write their name on the cover page and add a title. It may be "My Favorite Color Book," "My Favorite Color Is Green," "The Purple Book," etc. Encourage the children to decorate the front and back covers with their own personal touches.

7. Have the children carefully assemble the books. With young children you must be very certain that all their pages are in the correct position. Help the children place the front and back covers on the pages. Staple the books two or three times on the left-hand side.

8. Try to allow time for children to share their work. This may be done in front of the whole class, in small groups, or with partners.

ROY G. BV

Purpose:
Students create poetry using the vocabulary words.

Materials:
Colored paper (red, orange, yellow, green, blue, and violet), writing paper, pencils, small piece of poster board or large sheet of drawing paper, colored markers, glue (optional), scissors

Preparation:
1. Locate several pictures of rainbows. Posters and science books are possible sources for these photos.
2. Cut the colored paper into small squares. You will need one square of each color per student.
3. On the small poster write the capital letter "R" using a red marker, an "O" using an orange marker, a "Y" with yellow, a "G" with green, a "B" using a blue marker, and a "V" with a violet marker.

Procedure:
1. Show the class the pictures of rainbows. Ask them to describe the colors that they see.
2. Hold up the poster that says "ROY G. BV." Tell the class that even though this sounds like a man's name, it really is a special code. Explain to the class that this is the way to remember the order in which colors are found in the light spectrum. We can see the light spectrum when we look at a rainbow. A rainbow will always have the colors in this order. Ask students to name each color that the letters represent. Tell the class that scientists call the color purple violet.

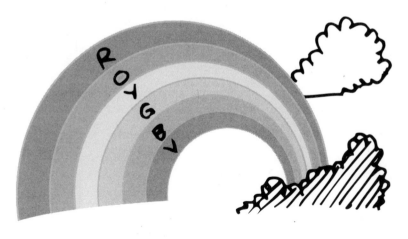

3. Have the children look at the pictures of the rainbow again. If they are photographs, have students try to point out the order of the colors. If they are drawings, ask the children if the artist drew the rainbow colors in the correct order.

4. Give each child the set of colored squares. Have the class put the squares in the correct order by using the name ROY G. BV. Then have the children mix up the color squares and place them in the correct order one more time.

5. Pass out a piece of writing paper to each child. Remind the class to write their names on their papers. Tell the children that they are going to write a type of poem using the letters ROY G. BV. Help the students write the letters in a vertical line down the left-hand side of their papers. Be sure to check that all students have written the correct letters in the proper order.

6. Tell the students that each of these capital letters will now become the first letter of one line in their poem. They are to think about things that have to do with the colors. Each sentence they write should be about the color that the beginning letter represents. Here is a sample:

> **R**ed is the color of apples.
> **O**range is my favorite color crayon.
> **Y**ellow makes me think about butter.
> **G**reen makes Kermit the Frog happy.
> **B**lue is the color of my eyes.
> **V**iolet would be a wild color for shoes.

Optional:
Let students glue their colored squares to their poetry papers.

Colorful Spelling

Spelling List Grades 1–2

red	blue	green	black	yellow	pink	white

Spelling List Grade 3

red	blue	green	yellow	pink	black	white	purple	orange	gray

Purpose:
Students will learn to spell color words using an enhanced visual technique.

Materials:
Drawing paper, writing paper, colored crayons or pencils, lead pencils, chalkboard and chalk or overhead projector and markers

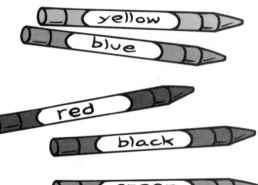

Procedure:
Session One:
1. Give each child a piece of drawing paper and access to the crayons.
2. Write the word "red" on the board. Ask students to find the red crayon and write the color word on their paper. Then write the word "blue" on the board. Have the students use a blue crayon to write the word on their papers. Continue in this manner until all the spelling words have been written. Note: For the word "white," have students write the word in pencil first, then trace over it with a white crayon.
3. Once all the words have been written, tell students to write each word at least two more times using the appropriate color crayon.

Session Two:
Give each child a piece of writing paper. Have students write a sentence for at least five of the words using the matching crayon each time they write a color word.

Session Three:
This session can be used for assessment. Give students a spelling test on the names of the colors. You may wish to hold up a matching colored square of paper for each color word you ask the students to spell.

Adding Color

Purpose:
Students will rewrite sentences using vocabulary words as adjectives.

Materials:
Pencils, worksheet (see next page), a variety of everyday objects

Preparation:
1. Collect a variety of everyday objects. You will need several sets of items that come in different colors, for example, different colored blocks, pencils, balls, stuffed toys, books, etc.
2. Make enough copies of the worksheet so that each child can have one. Or use the worksheet concepts to create your own worksheet using specific words you choose.

Procedure:
1. Spread the objects out where all the students can see them. Group the similar items together.
2. Tell the class to look carefully at the various items. Say to the students: *If I ask you to bring me the ball, you would not know which ball I wanted. But if I ask you to bring me the red ball, you would know what to do.* Ask a student to bring you a specific item. Then request a general item again. Reinforce the point that you need to better describe each item before a child can determine which object you are requesting.
3. Explain to the class that color words are describing words, or adjectives. These words help us to identify what is being described. They also help us to get a better picture of something when we are reading. Have students close their eyes. Ask them to think about a fish. Let students share the color of the fish they imagined. Point out that the class thought of many different kinds of fish. Now ask students to close their eyes and think about a small red fish. They will see how describing words create more specific pictures.

Assessment:
Give each child a copy of the worksheet. Explain the directions and provide enough time for students to complete the work.

Starting Points for Vocabulary © 2000 Monday Morning Books, Inc.

Name_____

Read each sentence. Where would it be good to add a color word? Use a word in the Word Box to rewrite each sentence. Be sure to put a color word in each new sentence you write.

Word Box

purple	red	blue	green	white
black	orange	yellow	brown	

Example: The dog is sleeping on the rug.
             The dog is sleeping on the **blue** rug.

The bird flew over the house.

_____

That car is going very fast.

_____

My shirt is dirty.

_____

The mouse ran away from the cat.

_____

The ball is not in the box.

_____

Pets

Vocabulary List

bird	cat	dog	ferret	fish
gerbil	guinea pig	hamster	horse	lizard
mice	rabbit	snake	turtle	

Activities:

1. Pet Parade—Students design floats for their favorite pet. The parade then becomes a lesson for using ordinal numbers.
2. Feature Analysis—Working with charts that analyze features helps students to cement their knowledge of the vocabulary words.
3. The First Dog—Or cat, or bird, or hamster. Students write stories about how the first pets came into being.
4. Pet Seminar—Children give short speeches about the care of pets.

Word Study Extension:

R-controlled Vowels—A worksheet helps students deal with this common consonant-vowel combination.

Starting Points for Vocabulary © 2000 Monday Morning Books, Inc.

Pet Parade

Purpose:
Students will associate vocabulary words with actual objects. They will read the words for ordinal numbers and correctly interpret the meaning of these words.

Materials:
Stuffed animals, shoe boxes, scissors, glue, poster board, markers, colored paper, fabric scraps, foil, crepe paper, streamers, etc.

Preparation:
1. You will need to gather at least 12 shoe boxes and 12 stuffed animals. The children should be able to bring in the animals to share for the activity.
2. Cut the poster board into strips. Use the markers to create 12 signs. Label each sign with an ordinal number (first, second, third, etc.).

Procedure:
1. Divide the class into 12 groups. Give each group a shoe box. Tell the children that they are to decorate the shoe box with the art supplies. Once the shoe boxes have been decorated, add a stuffed toy to each one to create animal floats for the parade.
2. Line up all the floats in the front of the room. Take the ordinal number signs. Read each sign with the class. Have a student place the word in front of the float that corresponds to the ordinal number. Continue until all of the floats have been labeled.
3. Tell the class that they are now going to change the order of the floats. Call on a student and give him or her a direction that requires reading the ordinal numbers and making a change in the parade.

Examples:
Put the elephant float in <u>second</u> place.
Move the red float to <u>twelfth</u> place.
Switch the animals in the <u>third</u> and <u>sixth</u> floats.

Feature Analysis

Purpose:
Students will develop and read a chart to analyze information based on vocabulary words.

Materials:
Teacher-generated worksheet, pencils, chalkboard and chalk or overhead projector and markers

Preparation:
1. Create a worksheet that contains a chart similar to the one below. Adjust the number of features according to the abilities of your class. Make a copy for each student.

Pet	Fur	Feathers	Tail	4 legs	Can Be Held
guinea pig	+	-	-	+	+

2. Write the following sample chart on the chalkboard or overhead:

Fruit	Round	Sweet	Yellow
banana			
lemon			
orange			

Procedure:
1. Tell the class that they need to think about all the characteristics of objects and words in order to use them correctly in writing. Have students look at the chart on the board and think about what the fruits look and taste like. Ask a child if a banana is round. When the answer is negative, place a - sign under the word "Round." Ask another child if the banana is sweet. For a positive answer place a + below the word "Sweet." Do the same for all of the categories and fruits.
2. Pass out the worksheets you have prepared. Ask students to think about the animals on the vocabulary list. They are to choose five animals and list them on the chart. Tell the class to think about the features listed on the worksheet and which of their animals has them. Remind students to place a - if the answer is "no" and a + if the answer is "yes."

40   *Starting Points for Vocabulary* © 2000 Monday Morning Books, Inc.

The First Dog

Purpose:
Students will write a story using the vocabulary words. They will also review the concepts of sequence of events and comprehension of the main idea.

Materials:
The First Dog by Jan Brett, writing paper and pencils, list of vocabulary words

Procedure:
1. Spend some discussion time talking about the children's pets or animals that the children would like to have. Ask the class why they think people like to have pets.
2. Read the book *The First Dog* to the class. Discuss the main idea of the story. Go over the sequence of events that occurred in the tale. Point out that this is one person's idea of how people began keeping pets.
3. Tell the children that they are going to write a story about how they think animals first became pets. Go over the vocabulary words with the students. Say: *You are going to write a story about how one of these animals became a pet for the very first time. You will have to imagine a time long ago. Try to use at least five vocabulary words as well as your animal name in your story. Remember that each story has a beginning, a middle, and an end.*
4. Provide time for students to work on their stories. Conference with each child to be sure the story follows a sequence of events. Edit spelling and grammar. Have children write a final draft of their stories.
5. Encourage students to read their finished tales to the class.

Pet Seminar

Purpose:
In this multi-faceted activity, students will classify animals, research information, organize ideas, and then make a presentation.

Materials:
Books on pets and animal care, poster board, drawing paper, markers or crayons, paper, pencils, list of vocabulary words

Preparation:
Gather a large supply of books about pets and animal care. If your school library does not have enough, try the public library. Some pet stores have free pamphlets that deal with these subjects.

Procedure:
1. Write the following categories on the board:
Birds   Fish   Reptiles   Large Pets   Rodents
Have students name types of birds that are pets. Do the same with the fish category. List the rest of the vocabulary words under the appropriate heading (Reptiles—lizard, snake, turtle; Large Pets—cat, dog, horse; Rodents—ferret, gerbil, guinea pig, hamster, mice, rabbit).
2. Divide the class into five groups; each will research one of the above categories. You can group children according to which type of pet they have or would like to have. You will probably want to subdivide the Large Pets group members into "cats" and "dogs." You may need to do the same to other groups if they're too large. Subdividing also helps to manage the use of the research materials. Students in each group may work on their own or in pairs to create their presentation.
3. Distribute the research materials to each group.
4. Tell the students that they are going to present a short speech about how to care for each of the pets in their group. The presentation should include three facts about the animal, a drawing of the pet, and a poster that tells at least five things to do to care for the pet, including the type of home, food, and exercise it needs.
5. Before the presentations are made, remind students to face the audience, speak loudly and clearly, and hold the visual aids so that all may see.

Name_____

You know that the word "cat" has a short **a** sound.
When the letter **r** comes after a vowel it changes the
sound the vowel makes. Example: cart.

   Look at the words below. Circle each word in
which the **r** changes the vowel sound.

star	bird	bridge	rat
ferret	fresh	corn	crazy
green	danger	gerbil	stir
hamster	spring	monster	turn
horn	track	rug	horse
yard	lizard	road	friend
rock	rabbit	turtle	dragon

Word Box

lizard	**horse**	**turtle**	**hamster**

Use a word from the Word Box to fill in each blank.

The _____ likes to run in a little wheel.

My _____ eats bugs and has a long tail.

We take turns riding on our _____.

The _____ swims in the water.

Contractions

The following list of contractions appears on the list of the 500 most frequently used words in children's writing.

Vocabulary List

can't	didn't	doesn't	don't	he's
I'd	I'll	I'm	isn't	it's
let's	she's	that's	they're	wasn't
what's	who's	won't	wouldn't	you're

The following are additional contractions that may be used with any of the activities.

aren't	couldn't	haven't	he'll	here's
I've	she'll	there's	they'd	they've
we'll	we're	we've	you'd	you've

Activities:

1. Contraction Triplets—Puzzle piece contractions match their individual components.
2. Dominoes—A matching game to teach the association between contractions and their components.
3. Contraction Clips—A manipulative to help students learn contractions.
4. Mystery Clues—A writing assignment that combines contractions and the skill of drawing conclusions.
5. Jokesters—Telling jokes improves oral vocabulary.
6. Stringers—Another manipulative to aid the comprehension of contractions and their word parts.

Word Study Extensions:

Worksheets require students to create, decode, and use contractions in context.

Starting Points for Vocabulary © 2000 Monday Morning Books, Inc.

Contraction Triplets

Purpose:
In this small-group activity, students must match contractions with their components.

Materials:
Poster board, scissors, markers, pencils, old crayons

Preparation:
1. Cut the poster board into 16 strips.
2. Using a marker, write a contraction in the very center of each strip. On either side of the contraction write its component parts. Draw a puzzle cut line on both sides of the contraction and cut apart (see the illustration below). Group all the contractions and all the components parts.
3. Take the paper off a crayon. Rub the side of the crayon over the sections containing contraction components. Do not color the sections with contractions.

Procedure:
1. This activity works best with four students. Spread out all the component parts of all the puzzles face down on the table in front of the group. Pass out four contraction sections to each child.
2. Each player draws one puzzle piece in turn. If the piece fits with one of his or her contractions, the player keeps it. If not, the piece is placed face down again on the table. Play continues in this manner. The first player to match up all four contractions with their correct component parts is the winner.

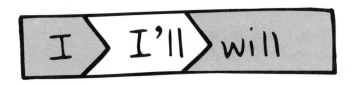

Dominoes

Purpose:
Students match contractions to their component parts while participating in a game.

Materials:
Blank index cards, ruler, markers

Preparation:
1. For each game set, you will need 40-45 index cards, or "dominoes." Draw a line across each index card to divide the space in half. On one side of the line, write a contraction. On the other side of the line, write any pair of words that make up any contraction.
2. If you wish the dominoes to be self-checking, use a different color marker for each type of contraction and its word parts. For example, all the contractions that are made up of a word plus the word "not" could be written in blue: wasn't, can't, didn't, etc. Then you would use the blue marker to write the matching component parts: was not, can not, etc.

Procedure:
1. Gather a group of three to five children. Pass out three dominoes to each child. Stack the other dominoes in a draw pile.
2. Take one domino from the draw pile and place it face up in the center of the table. The first player attempts to match either side of this domino with one held in his or her hand. If this is not possible, the player draws one from the pile and the turn ends. If the player is able to match the domino, it is placed on the table. Play continues in this manner until one person is completely out of dominoes. That person is declared the winner.

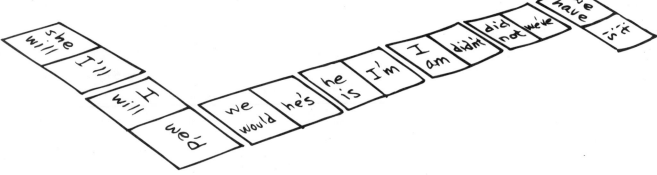

Starting Points for Vocabulary © 2000 Monday Morning Books, Inc.

Contraction Clips

Purpose:
This activity creates a manipulative that provides practice matching contractions with their component parts.

Materials:
Cardboard (recycled from boxes); markers; clip clothespins; scissors; small box, basket, or cloth bag

Preparation:
1. Cut the cardboard into various-size rectangles. With the rectangles positioned vertically, write the desired contractions down the center of the rectangle (see below). Leave at least one inch between the words.
2. Using a marker, write one component part of a contraction on each clothespin. Be sure to have all the component parts for all the contractions you have chosen. Place the clothespins in the small box.

Procedure:
1. This activity works best at a learning center. Place the cardboard rectangles and clothespins on a table. You may wish to make a sign that indicates the activity title and contains written instructions for use.
2. Let a student choose a rectangle. Tell the child to sort through the clothespins to find the two words that make up the contractions. When the correct words have been found, they should be clipped on the appropriate sides of the contraction. Students should find clothespins for all the words on a rectangle before choosing another rectangle.

Mystery Clues

Purpose:
Students will use contractions in spoken sentences. They must also listen carefully, then use divergent thinking to draw conclusions.

Materials:
Paper, pencils, list of contractions

Procedure:
1. Write the following sets of clues on the board. *This is something you **can't** use at school. It is something that's chewy. You put it in your mouth, but **shouldn't** swallow it. What is it?* (Answer: chewing gum.) *This **doesn't** have any legs. It usually **won't** make any sound. I **don't** like this kind of animal. I think **it's** creepy and crawly. What is it?*
2. Say: *I didn't tell you exactly what I was thinking about, but you were able to guess because I gave you clues. There is something special about the clues. What is it?* (Each contains a contraction.) Tell the class that they are going to write out clues just like those on the board. They should think carefully about how to describe something without giving away the answer. They must give at least three clues. Each clue must contain a contraction.
3. Give the students time to write their clues. Confer with each child to be sure that the words are spelled correctly and that they have underlined the contractions.
4. When all the students are finished, have them read their clues to the class. Let classmates guess the answers.

Starting Points for Vocabulary © 2000 Monday Morning Books, Inc.

Jokesters

Purpose:
Students will use contractions in context, carefully following the sequence of events to successfully tell a joke.

Materials:
Several books or children's magazines containing jokes and riddles

Procedure:
1. Read several jokes and riddles to the class. Choose those that include contractions, for example: "**What's** the difference between. . . "; "Knock, knock. **Who's** there?" Point out the contractions to the children. Explain the definition of "punch line." Have the children identify the punch line in several jokes. Try to include some longer anecdote-style jokes as well.

2. Tell the students that they are going to have a chance to tell jokes to the class. Discuss the following list of rules for telling jokes. You may want to make a poster of the list or make a printed copy for each child.

Rules:
• Jokes should never hurt a person's feelings or make fun of anyone in any way. Tell the joke to the teacher first to be sure it is a good joke for the class.
• Look at the audience when telling the joke.
• Know the order in which events happen in the joke.
• Don't laugh at your own joke until you have told the whole thing.
• Remember the punch line. Lead up to it, then deliver it quickly.
• Practice your joke until you can tell it smoothly with no mistakes.

3. Once all the jokes have been okayed and practiced, host a Comedy Hour in your classroom. Let children tell their jokes to the class. Invite your principal to attend and share a joke, too.

Stringers

Purpose:
Students will match contractions to their component parts and write contractions in sentences.

Materials:
Yarn (at least four different colors), scissors, glue, ruler, masking tape, cardboard or foam board, colored paper, pencils

Preparation:
1. You will need to create one stringer for every two to three students. Cut the cardboard into rectangles approximately 6" x 12" (15 cm x 30 cm).
2. Every three inches along the 12" (30 cm) sides, cut a 1" (2.5 cm) slit. Cut the yarn into 24" (60 cm) lengths. Use four different colors of yarn for each stringer. Find the center of each strand of yarn and tape it to the middle of the cardboard, spacing the strands about three inches apart.
3. Cut a piece of colored paper about 3" x 10" (7.5 cm x 25 cm). Write four contractions on this paper. These should be written in list fashion, again spaced about three inches apart. Glue this paper to the middle of the cardboard so that one strand of yarn is located under each word. (See the illustration.)
4. Above or next to each slit, write the components for the contraction. Be sure to mix up the locations of these components so that they are not next to the matching contraction. You can make the stringers self-checking by placing a colored dot on the back of the cardboard next to the corresponding color slit.

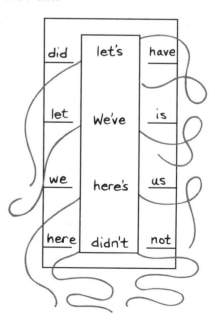

Starting Points for Vocabulary © 2000 Monday Morning Books, Inc.

Procedure:

1. Divide the class into small groups. Be sure each child has paper and pencil. Give one stringer to each group.

2. Tell the class that they are to look at each contraction. They need to find the word parts for each one. Once they have located the correct word parts they should put the strings of yarn into the corresponding slots. If you made the stringers self-checking, show the students how to check their answers.

3. Once the groups have matched all the contractions and word parts, they are to choose one contraction and use it in a sentence. Each person in the group may choose a different contraction if desired. Students may work together or individually to come up with the required sentences. Groups may exchange stringers or children may use them again individually at a learning center.

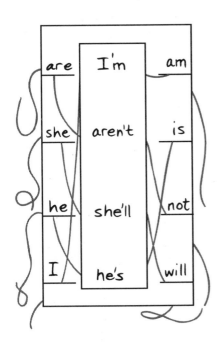

Name_____

Match each contraction with its parts. Write the matching letter on the line.

1. _____ can't   A. I will

2. _____ I'll   B. you are

3. _____ didn't   C. it is

4. _____ you're   D. I would

5. _____ I'd   E. did not

6. _____ it's   F. can not

Read each sentence. Circle the correct word.

1. This toy (won't   wasn't) fit in the box.

2. I think (let's   she's) ten years old.

3. Lisa (wasn't   doesn't) have any crayons.

4. He (wouldn't   don't) catch a snake.

5. (I'm   Let's) go to the park.

6. Please (don't   wouldn't) pop the balloons.

Starting Points for Vocabulary © 2000 Monday Morning Books, Inc.

Name_____

Write the contraction for each set of words. Use
the Word Box to help you.

Word Box

don't	they're	let's	wasn't	I'm	he's	wouldn't

1. do   not   _____   do ∫ not

2. let   us   _____   he ∫ is

3. I   am   _____   I ∫ am

4. was   not   _____   let ∫ us

5. they   are   _____   they ∫ are

6. he   is   _____   was ∫ not

7. would   not   _____   would ∫ not

Write a contraction in each blank. Use the Word Box to
help you. Remember to use a capital letter if you need one.

1. We _____ have any milk.

2. I think _____ getting a bad cold.

3. Did you know _____ moving?

4. _____ catching some bugs.

Weather

Vocabulary List

blizzard	breeze	cloudy	cold	fog
hot	humidity	hurricane	mild	rain
sleet	snow	storm	sunny	temperature
tornado	windy			

Activities:

1. Journals—This activity teaches the elements of record keeping.

2. Cloudy with a Chance of ?—Creative writing story starters.

3. Weather Windsocks—A craft project that illustrates word meanings.

4. Cloud Pictures—A dreamer's delight that combines an art project with a creative writing assignment.

5. Hurricanes and "Himacanes"—Stresses alphabetizing and proper nouns.

6. If . . Then . . .—This activity uses vocabulary words to help students develop complex sentences.

Word Study Extensions:

Spelling Worksheets—Utilizing weather words.

Grade 1—Students practice the spelling list by matching words and pictures and using words in context.

Grades 2-3—Students look at the structure of the spelling words and draw pictures to match words of their choice.

Journals

Purpose:
Students will use the journal format to practice writing dates and using vocabulary words in context.

Materials:
Writing paper, pencils, drawing paper, crayons, stapler, list of vocabulary words

Preparation:
1. The students need to have had a lesson on correctly writing dates. Children should know to capitalize the month and place a comma between the day and the year.
2. Make the journals. For each journal use five pieces of primary writing paper. Fold the pieces in half to form a booklet. Place a folded piece of drawing paper around the booklet for the front and back covers. Staple the left side to complete the journal. The journals may be made by the students if desired.

Procedure:
1. Pass out one journal to each student. Have the students write their names on the cover. Allow some time for them to decorate the front and the back.
2. Have the class open their journals to the first page. Help students to write the date on the first line. Decide whether you want the children to write phrases or complete sentences. It is recommended that first and second graders use phrase entries and third graders be required to write complete sentences.
3. Ask one student to announce the type of weather there is that day. Have students write this phrase or sentence under the date they have just written. Collect the journals and keep them in an accessible location. After several class sessions of filling out the journals together, encourage students to complete journal entries on their own after they arrive in class each day.

    Examples: September 17, 2000   sunny and windy
                September 17, 2000   Today's weather is
                                       sunny and windy.

Cloudy with a Chance of ?

Purpose:
Students will use vocabulary words to create an imaginative story.

Materials:
Cloudy with a Chance of Meatballs by Judi Barrett; writing paper; pencils; list of vocabulary words; colored paper; scissors; tinsel "icicles"; hole punch; yarn or string (optional)

Procedure:
Option I: Read the story *Cloudy with a Chance of Meatballs*. It is a funny story about a town where the precipitation is food. Encourage class discussion about other funny types of precipitation. Bring up the phrases "raining cats and dogs" and "When it rains, it rains pennies from heaven." Let children's imaginations run wild with possibilities. Then have the students write a story about an unusual weather occurrence. Remind the class to use as many vocabulary words as possible.

Option II: Talk about rainy days. Ask children what they do on days when they cannot go outside to play. Have students write a paragraph about how they spend a rainy day. Conference with children and have them edit their paragraphs. Cut out some large cloud shapes from gray paper. Let each child write his or her paragraph on the cloud. Add the "icicle" tinsel; it represents rain wonderfully. Punch a hole in the top of each cloud, add string, and hang the clouds around the room.

Option III: Have students write a poem about snow and cold. Let the children cut out snowflakes (fold paper, then snip out little shapes and open up). Mount the snowflakes on light blue paper. Have students rewrite their poems on the blue paper or, if possible, directly on the snowflakes. Punch a hole in the top of each paper, add string, and hang the snowflakes around the room.

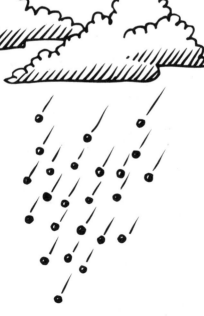

Starting Points for Vocabulary © 2000 Monday Morning Books, Inc.

Weather Windsocks

Purpose:
Students will illustrate the meanings of vocabulary words in this craft-making activity.

Materials:
Drawing paper, crayons or markers, crepe paper streamers, scissors, stapler, hole punch, yarn or string, list of vocabulary words

Preparation:
1. Cut the drawing paper into rectangles approximately 18" x 6" (45 cm x 15 cm). Be sure you have one rectangle for each student. You will also need small bits of drawing paper or colored paper that may be obtained from the scrap box.
2. Cut the crepe paper streamers into 18" to 20" (45 cm x 50 cm) lengths. You will need six for each child.
3. If desired, make a sample windsock by following the directions below.

Procedure:
1. Give each child a large rectangle. Have the students write their names on the rectangle. Then help them to print the words "Weather Words" in the center of the rectangle so the writing will be visible after stapling. Help them form the rectangle into a cylinder by bringing the ends together and stapling.
2. Give each child six pieces of scrap paper. Tell the children to cut the paper into interesting shapes. Then they are to choose six vocabulary words. Have them write one word on each shape, leaving room for an illustration. Under each word they should draw a picture that helps to show the meaning of the word. Each completed word picture is then stapled to a streamer. The streamers should then be stapled to the base of the cylinder.
3. Punch holes on both sides of the top of the windsocks. Tie on a loop of yarn and hang.

Cloud Pictures

Purpose:
Students will use divergent thinking and pictures they create to develop a story using vocabulary words.

Materials:
Photographs of clouds, blue paper, cotton balls, white glue, stapler, writing paper, pencils

Preparation:
Collect a wide variety of pictures showing clouds from magazines, travel photographs, science books, posters, travel brochures, and postcards.

Procedure:
1. Show the class the photographs of clouds. Ask them to use their imaginations to see shapes or faces in the clouds. Many students will be eager to share stories about "objects" they have seen in clouds. If the day is appropriate, take the class outside, lay on your backs, and do some cloud gazing.

2. Tell the class that they are going to create their own cloud scenes. Give each student a piece of blue paper and five or six cotton balls. Show the class how to stretch and pull the cotton balls to form clouds. Have students use a small amount of glue to attach the cotton balls to the blue background paper.

3. Once the pictures are complete, do a bit more cloud gazing. Ask students to think about what they see in the cloud pictures they have created. Then tell the children to write a story about what they see in their clouds. It might be how an animal got up in the sky, or that a certain guardian angel is watching over them, or just a story about a turtle because that's the shape they found in the clouds. When the stories have been edited and corrected, staple them to the cloud pictures.

Starting Points for Vocabulary © 2000 Monday Morning Books, Inc.

Hurricanes and "Himacanes"

Purpose:
Students will capitalize proper nouns and place words in alphabetical order.

Materials:
Writing paper, pencils, list of class names, book about hurricanes, chalkboard and chalk or overhead and marker

Procedure:
1. Read a bit about hurricanes to the class. Relate how hurricanes are given names so that they can be more readily identified as they are tracked. Tell the children that the names are given in alphabetical order: the first hurricane that develops is given a name that starts with a, the second hurricane is given one that starts with b, and so on. (You can obtain the current year's list of names from the National Weather Service.) Hurricanes used to be named only after women, but now men's names are also on the list.

2. Write the letters a-z on the chalkboard or overhead. Write the names of the children in class next to the letters they start with. Point out that each name is written with a capital letter because it is a proper noun. Indicate to the children that you now have an alphabetical listing for the class. Say: *If the Weather Service took names from our class, what would be the name of the first hurricane? How many hurricanes would there have to be to get to _____'s name?*

3. Tell the class that they are going to create their own list of hurricane/himacane names. Help the students write the letters a-z down the left side of their papers. Tell the children they may use some of their classmates' names or make up all the names themselves. They are to have only one name per letter (unlike your class list). Remind the students that each name must begin with a capital letter since it is a proper noun.

4. Once all the lists have been completed, keep them in a folder. Encourage students to learn about famous hurricanes (Camille, Andrew, etc.) and see if those names appear on any of the class lists. You can also monitor new current hurricane sightings to see if any names match the lists the children created.

If . . .Then . . .

Purpose:
Students will use vocabulary words to write complex sentences that illustrate their understanding of cause and effect.

Materials:
Paper, pencils, list of vocabulary words

Preparation:
Write the following sentences on the board:
>   If I am hungry, then I get something to eat.
>   If the baby cries, then Mommy will rock him.
>   If the sidewalk burns my feet, then it is hot.

Procedure:
1. Ask students to look at all of the sentences and determine what is the same in each one. (They all start with "If," there is a comma, they all contain the word "then," they all end with a period.)
2. Ask one student to read the first sentence. Talk about the cause and effect relationship. (The cause is "I'm hungry," the effect is "I get something to eat.") Do the same for the other sentences.
3. Tell the class that they are going to write "If . . then. . ." sentences. Each sentence must contain one of the vocabulary words. Assign a specific number of sentences (5-10). Remind students to begin each sentence with a capital letter and end it with a period. Help the children place the comma in the correct location, just before the word "then." Allow time for students to complete the assignment.

If the wind blows, then the leaves fall.

Name_____

Spelling Words

cloudy	cold	fog	hot
rain	snow	sunny	

Write the spelling word that tells about each picture.

_____

_____

_____

_____

_____

Read each sentence. Write a spelling word on the line.

1. It is hard to see when there is _____.

2. I can use my sled on the _____.

3. It is too _____ to go swimming.

4. The _____ helps make flowers grow.

For Grade 1

Name_____

Spelling Words

sunny	cloudy	sleet	mild
storm	blizzard	hurricane	
breeze	windy	tornado	

Write the words in ABC order. _____

_____

_____

_____

Write the words that have the letter z.

_____

Write the words that end with the letter y.

_____

Write the word that rhymes with wild. _____

Write the word that rhymes with feet. _____

Write the words that mean bad weather. _____

_____

Write a weather word on each line. Use the back
of the paper to draw a picture to show what
each word means.

For Grades 2–3

Starting Points for Vocabulary © 2000 Monday Morning Books, Inc.

Clothing

Vocabulary List

blouse	boots	coat	dress
hat	jacket	jeans	mittens
pajamas	pants	shirt	shoes
skirt	socks	sweater	vest

Activities:

1. Favorite Friends Fashion Show—Students use vocabulary words to describe what their favorite storybook characters are wearing.
2. Relay Race—This wacky game lets students relate the spoken vocabulary word to the actual object.
3. Catalog Creations—Students match up vocabulary words with magazine photos, then add descriptions.
4. Fashion Forum—Young designers get a chance to create their own fabulous fashions.
5. T-shirt Book Reviews—Readers design a paper t-shirt that tells about a book they have read.
6. What Do I Do?—Students read vocabulary words in context, then draw a conclusion from the statement (includes a worksheet).

Word Study Extensions:

1. Vowel Sounds Worksheet—This worksheet, designed for Grade 1, asks students to provide the correct vowel to complete the spelling of six vocabulary words.
2. Syllable Worksheet—On this worksheet, geared for Grades 2 and 3, students are asked to classify each vocabulary word by number of syllables.

Favorite Friends Fashion Show

Purpose:
Students will write descriptive sentences using vocabulary words.

Materials:
Paper, pencils, wide variety of children's books and magazines, chalkboard and chalk or overhead projector and markers, list of vocabulary words

Preparation:
Gather a large supply of children's books and magazines. Photo jackets from children's videos will also be helpful.

Procedure:

1. Ask students to think about one of their favorite characters from a book, story, or movie. Have several children describe a clothing item their character usually wears. Ask students to describe the character and the item in a complete sentence. Write some of these sentences on the board as examples.

    Examples:
    Winnie-the-Pooh always wears a red shirt.
    Mickey Mouse has on very big shoes.

2. Tell the class that they are going to write sentences about their favorite friends. Each sentence must contain one of the vocabulary words. Remind students that a sentence starts with a capital letter and ends with a period. Tell the class that they may look at the books and magazines to get ideas for their sentences.

3. Give the assignment of writing five to ten sentences, depending on the age and abilities of your class. Have students underline the vocabulary word in each sentence.

4. Once all the sentences have been completed, divide the class into several small groups. Within the groups, students should share their sentences and help each other edit their writing to be sure sentences are complete and properly punctuated.

Relay Race

Purpose:
In this game, students must carefully follow directions while matching vocabulary words to concrete objects.

Materials:
3 cardboard boxes, 3 of each clothing item in the vocabulary list

Preparation:
1. Gather the clothing items. These can be purchased cheaply at garage sales or scrounged from friends, neighbors, and colleagues. Be sure that the items are in a fairly large size. Children will be putting them on over the clothing they are wearing.
2. Place one of each clothing item in each of the three boxes.

Procedure:
1. Place the three boxes at the front of the room. Divide the class into three teams and assign one box to each team. Be sure that the children understand which team they are on and which box belongs to their team.
2. Tell the class that you are going to call out a direction. The first player on each team is to go to the team's box and carry out the instruction, putting on particular items of clothing. The first player to correctly complete the task earns two points for their team. All other players who correctly complete the instruction earn one point for their team. This keeps all players trying throughout the entire game.
3. Tell the students that when they follow a direction to put on an article of clothing they are not to take off any of their own clothing. The clothes in the boxes are big enough to put on over what they are wearing. Here are some examples of instructions for the game:

Put on two mittens and a hat.   Dress in a shirt and two shoes.
Dress in one boot and a skirt.   Put on the vest and a jacket.
Put on a sweater and pants.   Dress in a blouse and sweater.

Catalog Creations

Purpose:
Students will write descriptive sentences that match vocabulary words to pictures.

Materials:
Drawing paper, scissors, glue, stapler, pencils, old clothing catalogs and magazines, list of vocabulary words

Preparation:
Gather old catalogs and magazines. Ask students to bring some in from home. Some stores may be willing to donate catalogs to your classroom.

Procedure:
1. Give two sheets of drawing paper to each child. Have the children place one piece on top of the other and then fold the two papers in half to form a small booklet. Staple the left-hand side of the booklet to hold the pages together.
2. Show the class several examples from the catalogs. Point out that along with the pictures there are descriptions of each of the items. Tell the students that they are going to make their own catalogs.
3. Students should cut out pictures of clothing or people wearing different kinds of clothing from the catalogs and glue them into their booklets. Tell the class that they may mix and match parts of pictures to create wild and wacky outfits. Under each picture they should write a description of the fashion they have created. Each description must include at least one of the vocabulary words.
4. Show the class that the first page of the booklet should be their cover. They should come up with a name for the catalog and a design to go along with the name they have chosen. Students will have room for at least seven pictures and their descriptions on the rest of the pages. This should be the minimum assignment. Older students should be able to put at least two pictures on each page.

Starting Points for Vocabulary © 2000 Monday Morning Books, Inc.

Fashion Forum

Purpose:
Students will draw and label pictures of items on the vocabulary list, then explain their drawings to the class.

Materials:
Drawing paper, crayons, colored pencils, markers, list of vocabulary words

Procedure:
1. Give each child a piece of drawing paper and make pencils, crayons, and markers available.
2. Tell the class that they are going to design their own special clothing fashions. Students should draw a picture of a person wearing at least four of the items on the vocabulary list.
3. Help students to correctly label each item they have drawn.
4. Once the drawings are complete, hold a sharing time. Ask students to come forward, show their drawings, and explain their fabulous fashions.

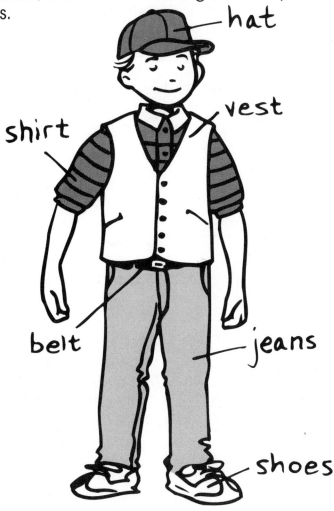

T-shirt Book Reviews

Purpose:
Students will read a story, summarize the contents, and use vocabulary words in context to present information about the story.

Materials:
Large pieces of blank newsprint, crayons, markers, pencils, scissors, wide variety of children's books, list of vocabulary words, recycled scrap paper

Preparation:
1. Cut t-shirt shapes from the newsprint. You will need one shirt for each student.
2. Gather a large selection of books that are in some way related to clothing. Some suggestions: *The Mitten* by Jan Brett, *500 Hats of Bartholomew Cubbins* by Dr. Seuss, *Alexander and the Terrible, Horrible, No Good, Very Bad Day* by Judith Viorst, *The Berenstain Bears at the Giant Mall* by Stan and Jan Berenstain, and *Little Ballerina* by Ann Morris.

Procedure:
1. Allow time for children to choose and read a book.
2. Tell the class that they are going to design a paper t-shirt that tells about the book they have just read. The t-shirt book review should include the following:

> title of book
> author
> list of characters
> a picture of a clothing item from the book
> three to five sentences that tell about the story
> one or two sentences that tell how the reader feels
> > about the book

Bonus points will be given for each vocabulary word used in the review.
3. Have students use the recycled scrap paper to prepare a rough draft of their review. Tell the students to plan where they will write or draw each requirement. Have them edit and correct their sentences.
4. Give each child a t-shirt shape so that they may design their final product.

Starting Points for Vocabulary © 2000 Monday Morning Books, Inc.

What Do I Do?

Purpose:
Students will read vocabulary words in context and draw conclusions.

Materials:
Pictures or drawings of community helpers, worksheet (see next page), pencils

Preparation:
1. Make enough copies of the worksheet so that each student will have one.
2. Gather pictures or drawings of people wearing specialized clothing, such as a police officer, firefighter, doctor, construction worker, person with raincoat and umbrella, etc.

Procedure:
1. Hold up one of the pictures. Ask the students if they can identify what the person in the picture does. Ask the students to tell why they were able to give their answer. Ask how the person's clothing helped them understand what the person does. Repeat this exercise with several pictures.
2. Read the following samples to the class. Discuss the answers.

> The boy is wearing a heavy coat and some boots. He has a hat on his head and mittens on his hands. Is he going to play in the snow or build a sandcastle?

> The woman is wearing a skirt and a blouse. She is carrying a stack of papers. Is she going to work in the garden or going to a business meeting?

3. Pass out the worksheets. Go over the directions with the class. Give the students time to complete the assignment.

What Am I Doing?

· ·

Name_____

Read the first group of sentences. Put a ring around
the words that tell what you think the person is doing.
Do the same for all the groups of sentences.

1. The girl is wearing a pretty dress and new shoes.
She is going to:

   a swimming pool   work in the garden   a birthday party

2. A man has on a hard red hat. He is wearing big
rubber boots and a large coat. He is a:

   firefighter   doctor   teacher

3. The boy is wearing shorts. He is NOT wearing
anything else. He is at:

   the dentist   the beach   a church

4. The woman has on jeans and an old shirt. She
has gloves on her hands and a straw hat on
her head. She is going to:

   work in the garden   a dance   sing at a wedding

5. The man is wearing jeans and a work shirt. He has on
a tool belt and a hard hat. He is going to help:

   bake a cake   build a house   teach a dance class

Starting Points for Vocabulary © 2000 Monday Morning Books, Inc.

Name_____

Fill in the missing letters.

a a a e i o o

1. h __ t

2. dr __ ss

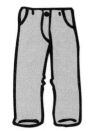

3. p __ nts

4. c __ __ t

5. sh __ rt

6. s __ cks

Write each word that you made 2 times.

1. _____   _____

2. _____   _____

3. _____   _____

4. _____   _____

5. _____   _____

6. _____   _____

blouse   **boots**   **jacket**   **jeans**   **mittens**
pajamas   **shoes**   **skirt**   **sweater**   **vest**

Write each word under the correct heading.

1 syllable	2 syllables	3 syllables
_____	_____	_____
_____	_____	_____
_____	_____	_____
_____	_____	_____
_____	_____	_____
_____	_____	_____

Circle each clothing word in the puzzle below.

Bugs

Vocabulary List

ant	bee	butterfly	caterpillar
cricket	dragonfly	firefly	flea
fly	gnat	grasshopper	hornet
ladybug	moth	spider	termite
tick	wasp		

Activities:

1. A Bug's-Eye View—This activity combines a craft project with a creative writing assignment.
2. Cursive Critters—Students stretch their imaginations while practicing cursive writing.
3. Insect Factoids—An introduction to research and non-fiction writing.
4. Creep and Crawl—This activity reinforces the identification and use of verbs.

Word Study Extension:

Verb Worksheet—Students use verbs in context as well as draw pictures illustrating verbs.

A Bug's-Eye View

Purpose:
Students will complete a crafts project, then write a story about it that includes vocabulary words.

Materials:
Cardboard egg cartons (one for every six children), scissors or craft knife (for the teacher), chenille craft stems, markers, paper, pencils, a storybook about bugs (*Ten Flashing Fireflies* by Philemon Sturges, *The Very Hungry Caterpillar* by Eric Carle, or books in the *A Bug's Life* series from Disney are good possibilities), list of vocabulary words, video of *A Bug's Life*.

Preparation:
1. Collect the egg cartons and cut off the tops.
2. Cut the cup sections into six pieces of two cups each. Cut out a small circle from the bottom of each cup.
3. On each side of each cup pair, poke a small hole. This is where the chenille stems go so children can wear the bug-eyed glasses.

Procedure:
1. Tell the children that they are going to pretend to be bugs. Ask the class to think about what a bug might see if it were on the floor of the classroom, in the grass outside, on a leaf in the tree, or sitting near a pond. Tell the class that they are going to make some bug eyes to help them imagine what a bug would see.

2. Give each child a pair of prepared egg cups. Allow time for the children to decorate and color them. Then help the children to attach the chenille stems by looping a stem through each hole and twisting the end around the main portion of the stem. Help the children gently position their bug eyes on their face, then curl the other ends of the stems around their ears. If desired, children can add additional curled chenille stems for antennae.

3. Let the children wear their bug eyes while you read them a bug story. This is a wonderful opportunity for picture taking. As an option you can also watch *A Bug's Life*, which provides an interesting look at the world through a bug's eyes.

4. Next, have the class write a story about what the world looks like from a bug's-eye view. Put the list of vocabulary words on the board. Ask the children to think about what each of those bugs might do in its daily life. Discuss the various possibilities as a group. Tell the students that when they write their stories, they are to include at least seven of the vocabulary words. Give students time to write. Help the students edit and make corrections. Allow another time period for the class to share their stories.

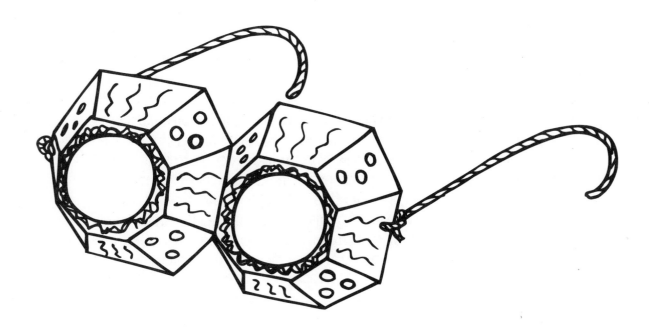

Cursive Critters

Purpose:
Students will practice cursive writing of vocabulary words in this artistic endeavor.

Materials:
Drawing paper; writing paper; pencils (be sure they are #2); crayons, colored pencils, or markers; list of vocabulary words; scissors

Preparation:
Cut the drawing paper in half. Each child will need two pieces of paper.

Procedure:
1. Give each student a piece of writing paper. Tell the students to write each of the vocabulary words in cursive. Tell the students to also practice writing their first names in cursive. Check to be sure that they are forming all the letters correctly. Have the students write their vocabulary words at least two times each and their first name at least five times.
2. Pass out two pieces of drawing paper to each child. Tell the class that one piece of paper is for their first name and the other paper is for a vocabulary word of their choice. Help the children to fold each piece of paper in half the long way.
3. Have the students open their first piece of paper. Tell the class that they are to write their first name along the fold in the paper. Have the students write in large, deliberate script. Remind the students to press down firmly as they write. If you notice that some children have written very lightly, ask them to trace over their name a second time.
4. Next, have the children fold the paper in half again. On the back of where their name was written, students should color over the entire paper with their pencils. This will serve to transfer their writing to the opposite side of the paper. Once this has been completed, have them open up the paper. They should see a mirror image of the cursive writing on the other half of the fold. Tell students to trace over the mirror image to make it more visible. Turn the completed image to a vertical position. It should look like an unusual insect.

Starting Points for Vocabulary © 2000 Monday Morning Books, Inc.

5. Now comes the fun part! Children should color in the shapes and spaces of the image. They may add eyes to one of the shapes. Also have them trace over the lines with crayon or marker. Encourage students to add stripes or spots to their drawings. When the drawings are completed, the students will have Cursive Critters.

6. Have the students repeat the process with one of the vocabulary words.

7. Cursive Critters make a wonderful bulletin board display. They are also a great conversation starter for Open House or Parent Night.

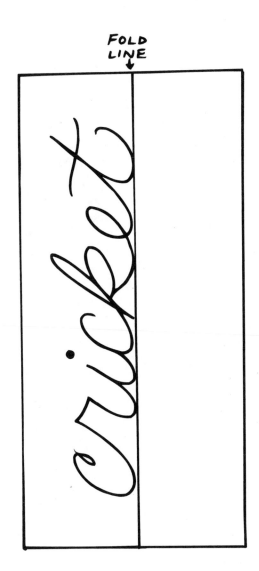

Insect Factoids

Purpose:
Students will research information and write a non-fiction report using vocabulary words in context. Students will also give an oral presentation.

Materials:
Paper, pencils, research materials about insects, list of vocabulary words

Preparation:
Gather materials for research or make arrangements to spend time in the school library. You will need a wide variety of sources for the children to use. Non-fiction books about insects, children's encyclopedias, and nature magazines such as *Ranger Rick, My Big Backyard,* and *Zoobooks* are possible resources.

Procedure:
1. Tell the students that they are going to find out some facts about a specific insect. Allow the children to browse through the materials before making a final choice on the subject of their report.

2. Explain the assignment to the class. The students are to:

> Choose an insect.
> Find out at least five facts about the insect.
> Write each of the five facts in sentence form.

Suggest to students that they try to find out the color of the insect, its size, what it eats, where it lives, and if it has any special abilities or features.

3. Remind the class that a sentence is made up of a complete thought, begins with a capital letter, and ends with a period.

4. Edit the writing assignments and help students to make corrections. When the writing has been completed, let each child read his or her report to the class.

Starting Points for Vocabulary © 2000 Monday Morning Books, Inc.

Creep and Crawl

Purpose:
In this activity, children will practice using verbs and vocabulary words in context.

Materials:
Paper, pencils, chalkboard and chalk or overhead projector and markers, several non-fiction books about insects

Procedure:
1. Ask one child to come forward and run a few steps. Write the word "run" on the board. Have another volunteer come forward and hop. Write the word "hop" on the board. Ask a child to come forward and sing. Write the word "sing" on the board. Then have the class look at the words on the board. Explain to the students that all these words are action words, or verbs.
2. Tell the students to take a few minutes to think about bugs. Ask the class to name some verbs that describe the actions of bugs. Here are some possible ideas: buzz, crawl, jump, glide, creep, fly, swarm, sting, wiggle, dig, bite, float, and hop. As the children brainstorm, write their words on the board.
3. Write the list of vocabulary words on the board. If you wish to extend the list, ask the class to name as many kinds of bugs as they can. Some possible additions to the list are aphid, centipede, cockroach, earwig, katydid, locust, mosquito, pill bug, scorpion, and weevil.
4. Ask the children to choose 10 of the bugs listed. Have them write each of these names in a list on their papers. Then tell the students that they are to write a verb that matches each bug. They may use a word from the list or another verb that applies.

Examples:
spiders crawl
grasshoppers jump
caterpillars creep

bees sting
dragonflies glide
gnats swarm

Name_____

Use the verbs in the Word Box to fill in the blanks.

Word Box

| chirping | glow | hop | make | sitting | sting |

1. Those ants are trying to _____ a hill.

2. I saw a flea _____ off the dog.

3. That bee might _____ you.

4. The butterfly is _____ on the flower.

5. The crickets were _____ all night long.

6. Fireflies _____ in the dark.

Draw a picture for each verb.

a caterpillar that wiggles

three birds flying

a child is jumping

a spider that crawls

Starting Points for Vocabulary © 2000 Monday Morning Books, Inc.

Size

Vocabulary List

big	giant	gigantic	huge	large	tall
little	miniature	short	small	teeny	tiny

Activities:

1. Big, Small, Best of All—A creative writing project that asks students to think about the advantages there are to being their exact size.

2. Pocket Pairs—A craft project that illustrates the vocabulary words.

3. Big and Little Books—A project that involves categorizing skills.

4. Search High and Low for Big and Little—Students read vocabulary words in context and use clues to find items around the room.

5. Fantastic Facts—This introduction to research skills helps students discover interesting facts about gigantic and tiny creatures.

Word Study Extension:

Synonyms Worksheet—Introduces children to the concept of synonyms.

Big, Small, Best of All

Purpose:
In this creative writing assignment, students will use vocabulary words in context.

Materials:
Drawing paper, writing paper, pencils, crayons or markers, *D. W. Thinks Big* by Marc Brown (one of the Arthur books), chalkboard and chalk or overhead projector and marker

Procedure:
1. Read the book *D. W. Thinks Big* to the children. Ask the class about the times that people told D. W. she was too small to do something. Talk about when it was important for D. W. to be tiny.
2. Ask the children about times when it is wonderful being small.
3. Discuss ways that the students now think of themselves as "big kids" and what they are able to do.
4. Put some of the discussion thoughts into written form on the chalkboard or overhead:

   Examples:

   I am big enough to wash my own hair.
   I am small enough for a piggy-back ride.

   I like being short enough to fit in my playhouse.
   I like being tall enough to ride my two-wheeler.

   I'm little enough to be scared of the dark.
   I'm big enough to answer the telephone.

5. Have students write a similar pair of sentences. Then ask them to draw a picture illustrating what they have written. Be sure to have the students share their thoughts and drawings with the class.

Pocket Pairs

Purpose:
In this art project, students will use vocabulary words in context and match vocabulary words to concrete images.

Materials:
Colored paper, pencils, scissors, white glue, yarn, masking tape

Preparation:
1. Create a sample project. Cut out one very large and one very small apple shape from red paper. Add a green paper leaf to each one. Write a descriptive sentence that contains a vocabulary word on each apple.

> Example:
> This is a gigantic apple.
> This is a teeny apple.

2. Cut out a square from red paper that is slightly bigger than the small apple. Put glue on three sides of the square and attach it to the large apple to form a pocket.
3. Using tape, attach a piece of yarn to the back of the small apple. Attach the other end of the yarn to the inside of the pocket on the larger apple. Place the tiny apple in the pocket on the large apple.

Procedure:
1. Show the class the sample you have created. Tell the children that they are going to create a similar Pocket Pair. They may choose any shape, animal, or object. Carefully explain the steps for creating a Pocket Pair. Remind students that each shape must be large enough to have the required sentence written on it.
2. Have students check with you before gluing the pocket in place. This will assure that it is done correctly. Young children will need assistance cutting the yarn.

Big and Little Books

Purpose:
In this activity, students will classify vocabulary words and relate them to objects.

Materials:
Large pieces of drawing paper, assortment of magazines, scissors, glue, stapler

Preparation:
1. Use about ten pieces of drawing paper for the Big Book. Stack the pages and staple the left-hand side to form the book.
2. Cut the drawing paper into squares. Stack these pages and staple the left-hand side to form the Little Book.

Procedure:
1. Show the class the larger of the two books. Ask the children to name the words from the vocabulary list that could describe the book. Tell the students that they are going to look for pictures in magazines that represent large objects. Appropriate pictures include airplanes, bulldozers, skyscrapers, elephants, the space shuttle, etc. Once an object has been found, it should be glued onto a page in the Big Book. An appropriate phrase that includes a vocabulary word should be added beneath the picture. Examples of phrases are "a gigantic airplane," "three huge elephants," "the massive space shuttle."
2. Next, show the class the Small Book. Ask the children to name the words from the vocabulary list that could describe this book. Tell the students that they are again going to look for pictures in magazines that represent very small objects. Some possible pictures for this category are flowers, a kernel of corn, a bug, a pin, a baby bird, etc. These pictures should be cut out and glued onto a page in the Small Book. An appropriate phrase that includes a vocabulary word should be added beneath the picture. Possible phrases are "five tiny bugs," "a wee baby bird," "a teeny kernel of corn."

Search High and Low for Big and Little

Purpose:
Students will use divergent thinking to understand vocabulary words in context.

Materials:
Clue Sheets (see Preparation), pencils

Preparation:
1. Create Clue Sheets that are appropriate for your classroom. You will need to describe objects in the room using a vocabulary word in each sentence. Leave a blank after the sentence so that the students can fill in the object they think the clue describes. Here are some sample clues and possible answers:

Find a huge round object. _____ (globe)
This large item has four tall legs.
_____ (table)
This piece of wood with a tiny point helps you write.
_____ (pencil)
Find a giant drawing of the United States.
_____ (map)
What small, round object must turn to work?
_____ (doorknob)

Write at least 10 sentences on the Clue Sheet. Make enough Clue Sheet copies to give one to each child.

Procedure:
1. Divide the class into pairs. Give each student a Clue Sheet.
2. Read through the clues together as a class. Then tell students they may start searching for the objects that match the clues. Let the children know that there may be more than one answer for each clue. If students are able to give a valid reason for their answers, try to accept them.
3. Allow plenty of time for the search. Have a class discussion about the answers.

Fantastic Facts

Purpose:
Students will research a concept related to a vocabulary word and present the information in a non-fiction writing assignment.

Materials:
Writing paper, pencils, wide assortment of non-fiction books

Preparation:
Gather a variety of non-fiction books about animals, bridges, buildings, etc., including children's books that feature top-ten lists of animals and things. *The Top 10 of Everything* by Russell Ash is excellent; the *Guinness Book of Records* may be used by older students.

Procedure:
1. Write the following sentences on the board:
> The blue whale is a pretty animal.
> The 100-foot-long (30 m) blue whale is the largest mammal on Earth.

Ask the class which sentence tells a fact about the blue whale and which tells how someone feels about the whale. Reinforce the concept with two more sentences:
> The tallest building in the world is the Sears Tower in Chicago, Illinois.
> The Sears Tower is awesome.

2. Tell the class that today they are going to write only sentences that state facts. They will use the books to help them find information. They may choose any one of the following assignments to produce Fantastic Facts.
> Write five facts about a massive animal.
> Write five facts about a tiny animal.
> Write one fact each about the smallest snake, bird, fish, lizard, and mammal.
> Write one fact each about the biggest snake, bird, fish, lizard, and mammal.
> Write one fact each about the biggest mountain, building, bridge, boat, and airplane.
> Write five facts about the largest planet.
> Write five facts about the littlest planet.

3. Staple all the papers together to form a Fantastic Facts book for the class.

Starting Points for Vocabulary © 2000 Monday Morning Books, Inc.

Name_____

Synonyms are words that mean the same or almost the same. The words "large" and "huge" are synonyms. The words "small" and "tiny" are synonyms.

Find a synonym for each of the following words. Write the matching letter on the line.

1. _____ happy   A. smile

2. _____ scream   B. mom

3. _____ grin   C. angry

4. _____ father   D. glad

5. _____ mad   E. cap

6. _____ hat   F. dad

7. _____ mother   G. yell

Write the synonym for each underlined word on the blank line. Use the words in the Word Box to help you.

Word Box

| huge | tiny | rest | snack |

1. Let's have a picnic by this <u>big</u> lake. _____

2. We will <u>nap</u> after our long hike. _____

3. Today we have oranges for our <u>treat</u>. _____

4. The <u>small</u> ducks are learning to swim. _____

Our Town

Vocabulary List

apartments	ballpark	bank	church
courthouse	factory	fire station	hospital
houses	library	museum	playground
police station	post office	restaurant	school
stores	theater		

Activities:

1. Box City—Students create a unique town of model buildings and label the areas with vocabulary words.
2. Word Webs—Students generate words and categorize them to create concept webs.
3. Where's George?—This guessing game provides clues about particular locations; the answers are vocabulary words.

Word Study Extension:

Compounds Worksheet—Students practice identifying and creating compound words

Box City

Purpose:
Students will create buildings from boxes, then label them with the vocabulary words.

Materials:
Scissors, colored paper, crayons or markers, glue, small boxes, material scraps, foil, scrap paper, tissue paper, cardboard scraps, old plain sheet (optional)

Preparation:
1. Ask students, friends, and colleagues to save small boxes for you. Some possibilities: milk cartons, gelatin/pudding boxes, animal cracker boxes, margarine tubs, butter boxes, cheese boxes, orange juice cans, bandage boxes, etc. You will need at least one box for each child.
2. Cut the scrap paper into small squares. You will need one square for each child. Write one vocabulary word on each paper. If you have a large class, write houses, apartments, and stores on several more squares.

Procedure:
1. Tell the class: *We are going to create our very own town. A town needs many different kinds of buildings and places. We would not want to live in a town with all stores and no houses. It would not be much fun to have all factories and no parks or restaurants. I will give you each a scrap of paper. It will tell what kind of building or place you will need to make for our town.*
2. Say: *You will use the boxes and supplies to make your building or location. Cover the box with colored paper. Use the other supplies to add details. Write the name of your building on your project.*
3. If you are using an old sheet, let students draw streets on it with markers. You might want to glue green material to the sheet for a ballpark or playground. Children may then arrange the buildings on the sheet.
4. If you do not have a sheet, a large piece of newsprint can be substituted. Or children may simply place the buildings on a table top or in a corner on the floor.

Word Webs

Purpose:
Students must generate words and categorize them correctly in order to create concept webs.

Materials:
Large pieces of drawing paper, pencils or markers, picture of a large spider web, scrap paper, chalkboard and chalk or overhead projector and marker

Procedure:
1. Show the class the picture of the spider web. Point out how each strand is related to the other strands. Let students see that the web stretches out from one central point.
2. Tell the children that you are going to show them how to create a web using words. Choose one of the vocabulary words and write it in the center of the board or overhead screen. The sample here uses the word "school."
3. Ask the children to name all the kinds of people that are in the school (teachers, students, principal, secretary, aides, lunchroom cooks, janitor, etc.). Write these words on the web branching off from the word "people."
4. Ask students to name rooms in the school (classrooms, gym, cafeteria, office, library, storerooms, etc.). Write these words on the web.
5. Have students list things found in each of the rooms (desks, books, basketball hoops, bleachers, tables, chairs, etc.). Write these next to the appropriate rooms in the web.
6. Now tell students to choose one of the vocabulary words and create a web for that word. Have students write their webs on scrap paper first and conference with you for accuracy. Then have the children make the final copy of their word webs on the larger pieces of paper.

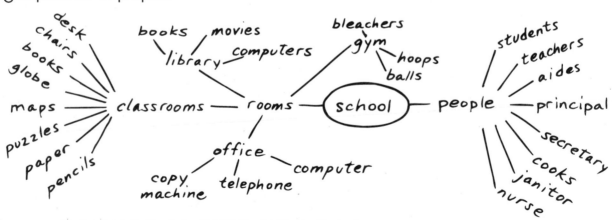

Starting Points for Vocabulary © 2000 Monday Morning Books, Inc.

Where's George?

Purpose:
Students will draw conclusions from clue sentences using vocabulary words and concepts.

Materials:
Index cards, pencils, poster board, markers, scissors

Preparation:
1. Cut the poster board into strips about 4" x 12"
(10 cm x 30 cm). Fold the strips in half lengthwise to create a free-standing sign. Write one vocabulary word on each sign.
2. Use one of the strips of poster board to create a tall sign. Draw a stick figure on this sign and label it "George."

Procedure:
1. Distribute the index cards.
2. Give one sign to each child or small group of children. Tell the students that they are to think of three clues that describe the word on the sign. Have the students write their clues on an index card.

> Example: library
> This place is free for everyone in town.
> You need a card to take something from this place.
> The building is filled with books.

3. Collect all the clue cards and put them in a pile. Spread out the signs in various locations in the room.
4. Ask one student to come forward and hold George. Draw one index card from the pile and read the clues to this student. Have the student place George next to the sign that tells where he or she thinks George is.
5. Ask another child to come forward and choose a card. Read the clues aloud. Ask the child, "Where is George now?" Let the student move the figure of George to the new location. Continue in this manner until all the clues have been read and George has been moved to each location.

Name_____

A compound is a word that is made from two other words. A compound can be written as one word—"baseball"—or as two words—"hot dog."

Word Box

apartments	ballpark	bank	church
courthouse	factory	fire station	hospital
houses	library	museum	playground
police station	post office	restaurant	school
stores	theater		

Look at the words in the Word Box. Find the compounds. Write each compound.

_____

_____

Write a compound for each picture set.

Example: _snowman_

1. _____

2. _____

3. _____

4. _____

5. _____

Starting Points for Vocabulary © 2000 Monday Morning Books, Inc.

Numbers

Vocabulary List

one	two	three	four
five	six	seven	eight
nine	ten	eleven	twelve
thirteen	fourteen	fifteen	sixteen
seventeen	eighteen	nineteen	twenty

Activities:

1. Chubby Numbers—Large cut-out shape posters help students to think about numbers in a creative fashion.
2. Time Lines—Students develop personal time lines.
3. Picture Count—Colorful illustrations help students generate sentences that include the vocabulary words.
4. Super Search—The students take part in a newspaper scavenger hunt.

Word Study Extensions:

Following Directions Worksheet—Students add to illustrations by following directions that include a number word.
Spelling Numbers Worksheet—This worksheet is designed to help students master the spelling of the vocabulary words. Each task requires the students to take a closer look at the letters used to spell each word.

Chubby Numbers

Purpose:
Students will use divergent thinking and vocabulary in context to develop number posters.

Materials:
Large pieces of colored paper, markers, scissors, writing paper, pencils, chalkboard and chalk

Preparation:
You may wish to create patterns for the large number shapes. Children may then trace the patterns and cut out the desired numbers. As you make the patterns, be sure that the numbers are thick and wide to allow plenty of room for writing.

Procedure:
1. Write the numbers 1-9 on the board. Ask the children to think of things that are usually found by themselves. For example, we have only one sun, there is one ace of hearts in a deck of cards, there is one principal at the school, etc. Spend some time discussing each number. For example, for the number five you might discuss fingers on one hand, cents in a nickel, players on a basketball team, etc.
2. Have the students each choose a number. Then ask them to each list at least 10 things that relate to that number. The children's answers may be personal, for example, for the number three a child might list three brothers, Grandpa's three cars, etc.
3. Once the lists have been completed, help the students to cut out the chubby shape of the number they have chosen from a large piece of colored paper. Have the children rewrite their lists on the number shapes.

Time Lines

. . . .

Purpose:
Students will use vocabulary words in context, organize a sequence of events, and write complete sentences as they make a time line of their lives so far.

Materials:
Newsprint roll, paper clips, markers or crayons, writing paper, pencils, scissors

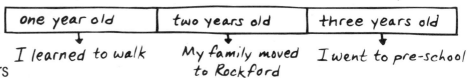

Preparation:
1. Locate an end roll of newsprint. These are the leftovers that are too small to complete an entire press run and are often available from your local newspaper office free of charge. End rolls are a wonderful resource that can be used in a variety of ways.
2. Cut the newsprint into strips approximately 6" x 6' (15 cm x 2 m). For ease of handling, roll each strip and secure with a paper clip. You will need one strip for each child.

Procedure:
1. Say to the class: *You are going to make a time line about your life. A time line lists important dates and events that happened during a period of time. I want you to take some time to think about each year of your life. Something special happened during each year. If you don't remember things from when you were very little, think about stories that family members or friends have told you.*
2. Say: *On your writing paper, write your age for each year of your life and something that happened at that age. Here is a sample.* Write the following on the board:

> one year old—I learned to walk.
> two years old—My family moved to Rockford.
> three years old—I went to preschool.
> four years old—My dog had puppies.
> five years old—I went to kindergarten.
> six years old—I read a whole book all by myself.
> seven years old—My soccer team won the big game.

3. Conference with the students to be sure they have used correct spelling and sentence structure. Give each child a long strip of newsprint. Show the class how to write the numbers and sentences in a time line. Students should then illustrate each event they listed.

Picture Count

Purpose:
Students will use vocabulary words in sentences to describe objects in a picture.

Materials:
Paper, pencils, wide variety of picture books (see Preparation), list of vocabulary words

Preparation:
Gather a wide variety of books that contain complex illustrations. Books from the *I Spy* or *Where's Waldo?* series work very well. Any stories illustrated by Jan Brett are also recommended for this activity.

Procedure:
1. Give one picture book to each child or pair of children.
2. Tell the class that they are to look very carefully at one page in the book. The students are to write one sentence for each object or set of objects that appear in the illustration. (You may need to set a limit of 5 to 10 sentences for young writers.) Each sentence should contain a different vocabulary word. Students should try to use only one picture in the book but, depending on the illustration, may use another page as well.

Examples:

There are three elephants near the water hole.
Four crocodiles are swimming in the river.
The five lions are all sitting under the tree.
There are six trees by the river.
Seven birds are flying in the sky.
I can see eight rocks in the picture.

Starting Points for Vocabulary © 2000 Monday Morning Books, Inc.

Super Search

Purpose:
Students will use the concept of skimming to read vocabulary words in the newspaper.

Materials:
Crayons or markers, newspapers, list of vocabulary words

Procedure:
1. Divide the class into four groups. Give one specific crayon color to each group—you will have a blue group, a green group, a red group, etc. The children may stay in their own seats for this activity. Their team is simply identified by the color of their crayons.

2. Show the children several pages of a newspaper. Say to the class: *In this game you are going to try to find as many numbers or number words as you can. You do not have to read ALL of the words on the page. That would be much too hard. You are going to "skim" over the page. Look at the bold, large-type words. These are called headlines. Try to find number words in the headlines. Other pages in the newspaper show advertisements. Stores and people are trying to sell things. This is a good place to look for numbers and number words, too. Another good place to look is in the sports section. When you find a number or a number word, circle it with your crayon.*

3. Give each child several pages of a newspaper. Allow 10 to 15 minutes for the scavenger hunt. When the time is up, have each team gather together and count up all the words and numbers that they have found.

Follow the directions. Read carefully.

Draw <u>two</u> ears
on the head.

Draw <u>four</u> fish in
the tank.

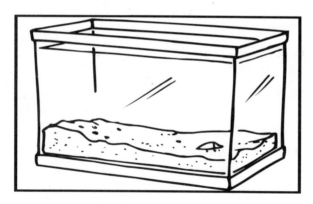

Draw <u>six</u> flowers in
the pot.

Draw <u>eighteen</u> dots
on the bug.

Draw <u>eleven</u> jelly
beans in the jar.

Draw <u>twelve</u> eggs
in the basket.

Name_____

Use the Word Box to help you complete the worksheet.

Word Box

one	two	three	four	five
six	seven	eight	nine	ten
eleven	twelve	thirteen	fourteen	fifteen
sixteen	seventeen	eighteen	nineteen	twenty

1. Write the words with **ee**. _____

_____

2. Write the words with a **v**. _____ _____

_____ _____ _____ _____

3. Write the words with an **x**. _____ _____

4. Write the words with a **w**. _____

_____

5. Write the word next to each number.

10 _____   8 _____

9 _____   4 _____

1 _____   15 _____

20 _____   13 _____

Onomatopoeia*

Vocabulary List

bang	boom	buzz	chirp
clang	click	crash	crunch
ding	honk	plop	purr
rattle	roar	screech	splash
squeak	thump	whir	zoom

Activities:

1. Comic Noise Collages—Students find sound words in comic strips.
2. Bang, Boom, Brainstorm—A board game that stretches children's thinking skills.
3. Sound Excursion—A no-cost mini-field trip that promotes careful listening.
4. "Ding-y" Inventions—Children's imaginations have free rein when they make crazy creations that illustrate onomatopoeia.

Word Study Extension:

Plurals Worksheet—This worksheet helps students to spell plurals with -es.

* Children love to say the word "onomatopoeia." They also enjoy the challenge of learning to spell this vowel-laden word.

 Starting Points for Vocabulary © 2000 Monday Morning Books, Inc.

Comic Noise Collages

Purpose:
Students will identify vocabulary words in context.

Materials:
Newspaper comics pages, scissors, glue, large pieces of newsprint, list of vocabulary words, chalkboard and chalk or overhead projector and marker

Preparation:
1. The comics are a fabulous source of onomatopoeia examples. Ask students to bring in some comics pages from the newspaper. Gather extras from colleagues and friends.

Procedure:
1. Write several or all of the vocabulary words on the board or overhead. Tell the children that onomatopoeia is the forming of words that imitate sounds. Spend some time letting children read the words and create the sounds. This will be noisy, but lots of fun. Encourage the class to think of other sound words that are not listed.
2. Tell the class that sound words can add a great deal of Puppy Power (see p. 12) to their writing. When a cartoonist draws a comic strip, he or she uses onomatopoeia to help the reader understand what is happening. The words help to make the cartoon even funnier.
3. Pass out several comics pages to each student. Do not pass out glue or scissors yet. Ask the children to look over the cartoons and try to find a sound word or example of onomatopoeia. Share some of these with the class.
4. Tell the class that they are going to cut out any cartoons that show onomatopoeia. Have students cut out the examples and glue them to newsprint to create a collage. Remind children that they need only a small amount of glue.

Bang, Boom, Brainstorm

Purpose:
Students use vocabulary concepts and divergent thinking in this small-group game.

Materials:
Index cards, markers, scissors, game boards (see Preparation), game tokens (plastic chips, pennies, old game markers, etc.)

Preparation:
1. For each group of students you will need one game kit. A game kit consists of 10 index cards cut in half, one game board for each child, and one game token for each child.
2. Cut the index cards in half. Write one vocabulary word on each half. You may extend the vocabulary list and write more cards if desired. Make a copy of the game board (see the next page) for each student.

Procedure:
1. Divide the class into small groups. Give one game kit to each group.
2. Explain the rules of the game. Each player should take one game board and one token. The index card halves should be placed face down in the middle of the group. The first player puts his or her token in the Start box, then draws a card and reads the word. The player then names as many things as possible that would make that sound. For example, for the word "squeak" responses could be "doors," "guinea pigs," "baby toys," and "mice." The player then moves the token ahead the same number of squares as the number of words given. In the above example, the player would move the token four spaces, the same number as the words given. If the space where the token lands gives directions, the player must follow the directions to complete his or her turn. If the space is blank, the player's turn ends. Play continues in this manner until one person reaches the Finish box.
3. If a player says a word that the others don't agree makes the sound, the player should explain. For example, a player might give the word "snow" for the onomatopoeia word "crunch." The group may think that snow comes down quietly, but the player might have been thinking about walking on cold, dry snow and hearing the crunch. If, after an explanation, the others still don't agree with the player, they should all check with the teacher.

Bang, Boom, Brainstorm Game Board

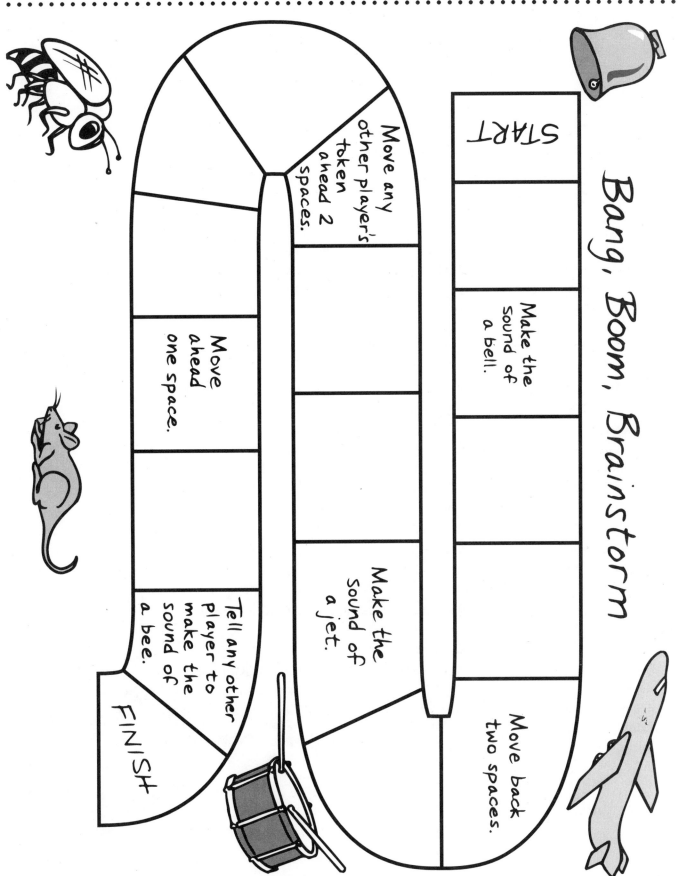

Bang, Boom, Brainstorm

START

Make the sound of a bell.

Move back two spaces.

Make the sound of a jet.

Move any other player's token ahead 2 spaces.

Move ahead one space.

Tell any other player to make the sound of a bee.

FINISH

Sound Excursion

Purpose:

Students will categorize sounds they collect in an active listening endeavor.

Materials:

Paper, pencils, clipboards (if clipboards are not available, cut cardboard to the size of the writing paper and attach to the paper with two paper clips), chalkboard and chalk or overhead projector and marker

Procedure:

1. Give a clipboard, paper, and pencil to each child. Tell the class: *Today we are going to take a trip. We are not going to look for things on this trip. Instead we are going to be listening. I want you to listen very carefully as we take our walk. Write down any sounds that you hear. Don't worry about spelling things correctly now. We can fix spelling later. You will all need to be VERY QUIET as we walk. In fact, we want to be so quiet that no one will know we are walking by. Then we can hear even more sounds.*

2. As you walk around the school building, be sure to visit a variety of areas. Go by the gym, art room, music room, cafeteria, office, library, etc. If possible, continue the walk for a short distance outside the school grounds. Stop often for children to write down the sounds they hear. Keep a list yourself to help with the discussion later on.

3. When you return to class, begin to categorize the sounds. Write the following or similar headings on the board or overhead: People Sounds, Machine Noises, Animal Sounds, Other. Have the children share the sounds they collected. Write each under the proper heading.

4. If desired, follow up the Sound Excursion with a writing assignment. Some story starters might be: "The Noisiest Day at School," "The Time All Sound Stopped," "Did You Hear That Weird Noise?", "The Day Our School Squeaked" (Buzzed, Rattled, etc.).

Starting Points for Vocabulary © 2000 Monday Morning Books, Inc.

"Ding-y" Inventions

Purpose:
Students will first develop an imaginative art project, then use vocabulary words in a creative writing project based on their artwork.

Materials:
Heavyweight drawing paper or brown grocery bags, writing paper, pencils, scissors, glue, crayons, markers, yarn, fabric scraps, foil, brad fasteners, paper clips, buttons, dot stickers, list of vocabulary words

Preparation:
1. Brown grocery bag paper makes an excellent base for this project. Cut the bottom off the bags, then cut the remaining paper into three or four sections.
2. Collect a variety of crafts supplies like the materials mentioned above.

Procedure:
1. Tell the children that this project has two parts. The first part is to create a very noisy invention. The second part will be to write a story about the invention. (Do the activity in two sessions.) Tell the children that they may make any type of invention. The only rule is that the invention may not be used to hurt anyone or anything. Here are some ideas to jump-start their imaginations: a time machine, an old, junky jalopy, an alien spaceship, a house that cleans itself, a robot, a bicycle with a built-in snack machine.
2. Make all the supplies available. Allow plenty of time for children to make their inventions.
3. Encourage the students to chat about their inventions in small groups or with a partner. This will help students organize their thoughts for the writing portion of the activity.
4. Have students write a story about their inventions. Require that at least seven vocabulary words appear in the story. Take time to conference with the students and have them edit and rewrite their work.

Name_____

When a word ends with z, s, x, sh, or ch, add -es to make it mean more than one (plural).

Add -es to each of the following words. Then write the new word on the line.

glass_____   _____

screech____   _____

buzz____   _____

splash____   _____

crunch____   _____

crash____   _____

box____   _____

pass____   _____

mix____   _____

Use the Word Box to help you fill in each blank.

Word Box

boxes	buzzes	crashes	splashes

1. The whale made three giant _____.

2. We have five _____ of cookies.

3. There were many car _____ in that cartoon.

4. Those bees are making loud _____.

Starting Points for Vocabulary © 2000 Monday Morning Books, Inc.

Emotions

Vocabulary List

angry	bored	calm	confused
embarrassed	excited	frustrated	happy
grumpy	lonely	loving	mad
proud	sad	scared	shy
surprised	worried		

Activities:

1. Emotion Meter—A craft project that becomes a spring-board for discussion about feelings.
2. Godzilla Meets A Kitty—This oral communication activity provides plenty of story starters.
3. A Picture of Happiness—Students relate photographs to their understanding of emotions.
4. Say It with Feeling—Students associate gestures and body language with specific emotions.

Word Study Extension:

Two Sounds of /y/ Worksheet—A coloring worksheet.

confused   bored   grumpy   excited   embarrassed   calm   frustrated

Emotion Meter

Purpose:
Students will relate vocabulary words to symbols and use these to discuss feelings.

Materials:
Poster board, hole punch, yarn, scissors, glue, crayons or markers, list of vocabulary words, scrap paper, chalkboard and chalk

mad

proud

scared

Preparation:
Cut the poster board into rectangles approximately 6" x 12" (15 cm x 30 cm). You will need one rectangle for each child. Punch a hole in the upper right corner of each rectangle and another hole in the lower right corner.

Procedure:
1. Write the list of vocabulary words on the board. You may wish to limit the list to about 10 words for this project. Next to each word draw a simple face that portrays each emotion (see the illustrations). Tell the children: *A thermometer tells us what the temperature is each day. We are going to make Emotion Meters that show how we feel during the day.*
2. Give each child a piece of poster board. Have the children choose five or six of the vocabulary words. Have them list these down the left side of their poster board. Ask the students to space the words so that they can illustrate each emotion.
3. Thread a piece of yarn through the holes and tie it in the middle. Be sure the knot is on the front side of the poster board. Let the students cut an arrow shape from a piece of scrap paper and glue it over the yarn knot.
4. Say to the class: *How do you feel when it is your birthday?* Show the class how to gently slide the arrow so that it points to the desired emotion. Continue asking questions that should bring out a variety of feelings.
5. The Emotion Meters may be used in other ways. Students could indicate how a character feels throughout a reading selection. They could also use the meters to convey what they are feeling when they are acting out or having problems with behavior. The meters could be utilized when there is a discussion about a current event or a disturbing local happening.

 Starting Points for Vocabulary © 2000 Monday Morning Books, Inc.

Godzilla Meets A Kitty

Purpose:
This two-fold activity promotes oral communication about emotions. It also provides an opportunity for students to use vocabulary words in context in a creative writing assignment.

Materials:
Writing paper, pencils, index cards, markers, list of vocabulary words, chalkboard and chalk

Preparation:
Write each of the following words on an index card.

Godzilla	kitty	ghost	blizzard	thunder
rainbow	angel	treasure	prize	birthday
shark	magic	diamond	baby	school
holiday	spider	snake	gold	dragon
champion	dinosaur	miracle	puppy	pillow
dark	beach	monster	war	tornado
hurricane	blanket	present	hospital	dentist

Procedure:
1. Write the vocabulary words on the board or be sure each child has a list. Say to the class: *Sometimes just thinking about one single thing or word can make us feel strong emotions.* Pick one index card. Say: *How does it make you feel when you hear and think about the word "Godzilla"? Use one of the vocabulary words to tell how you feel.* Discuss several different responses. Point out to the children that not all people will have the same responses. Reassure children that there are no right or wrong answers in this discussion.
2. Divide the class into five groups. Give several index cards to each group. Let the students continue a similar discussion in the small groups.
3. Have the students return to their seats. Give one index card to each child. Ask the children to write a short story about the word they have been given. Tell the class they may use some of the ideas that have been discussed. Require that at least three vocabulary words be used in the stories.

A Picture of Happiness

Purpose:
Students will use vocabulary words to describe pictures and write complete sentences using vocabulary words in context.

Materials:
Magazines, scissors, glue, writing paper, pencils, drawing paper, list of vocabulary words

Preparation:
You will need a large supply of magazines that contain photographs of people. Sports magazines, news weeklies, and entertainment periodicals work well for this project.

Procedure:
1. Choose several photographs from the magazines. Hold one up for the class. Ask the children how the person in the picture is feeling. Determine which of the vocabulary words best describes the picture. Do this with each of the photographs.
2. Give each child a sheet of drawing paper and a magazine. Tell the students that they are to find six different photographs in the magazines. Each picture should portray a different emotion. Have the students glue the photographs to the drawing paper. Each picture should be numbered and a vocabulary word written underneath it to describe the emotion.
3. On writing paper the children should write a sentence or two about each photograph to tell how the person in it is feeling and why he or she might be feeling that particular emotion. The sentences should be numbered to match the pictures.

    Examples:
1. The man just won the race. He is very proud.
2. This old woman is sad because her house burned down.
3. The children are very happy. They are splashing in the fountain on a hot day.

Say It with Feeling

Purpose:
Students will learn about non-verbal communication; they will
also practice reading with expression.

Materials:
Index cards, markers, list of vocabulary words

Preparation:
1. On index cards, write suggestions for using body language to
portray emotions. Here are some ideas:
angry—shake your fist
excited—jump up and down with arms in the air
confused—scratch your head
mad—put hands on hips
scared—sit in a little ball and shake
surprised—spread arms out, open mouth wide
proud—strut around with head high, shoulders back
loving—arms folded
calm—pretend to pet a kitty in your arms
bored—flop in a chair and yawn
worried—bite your nails
2. Write sentences and instructions for saying the sentences in a
specific manner. Here are some samples:
>Read this in a happy way: I am getting a new bike.
>Read this in a sad way: My dog ran away.
>Say this in an excited way: Our class is going on a field trip to the zoo!

Procedure:
1. Say to the class: *Sometimes we can know how people are feeling by
looking at the way they move their body. They don't need to say any
words at all. We are going to try to guess how a person feels just by looking
at what he or she is doing.* Have a child come forward and choose one of
the cards, then act out the emotion. Let the class guess which of the
vocabulary words the person is portraying.
2. Say to the class: *The way a person uses his or her voice can also help us
understand emotions.* Say this in a small, shaky voice: *My mom isn't home
yet.* Then say: *That tells you I am worried and a little scared. But if I say it this
way (use an excited, happy voice)—My mom isn't home yet!—that shows
that I am happy and maybe thinking about having a sweet, messy snack
without my mom knowing.* Have a child choose one of the cards listing
ways to say sentences. Ask the student to read the sentence. Have the
class guess which emotion is being portrayed.

Two Sounds of /y/

Name _____

In a one-syllable word in which /y/ is the only vowel sound, the /y/ makes the long i sound. When a two-syllable word ends with a /y/, the /y/ usually makes the long e sound. Color the long e sound words red. Color the long i sound words blue.

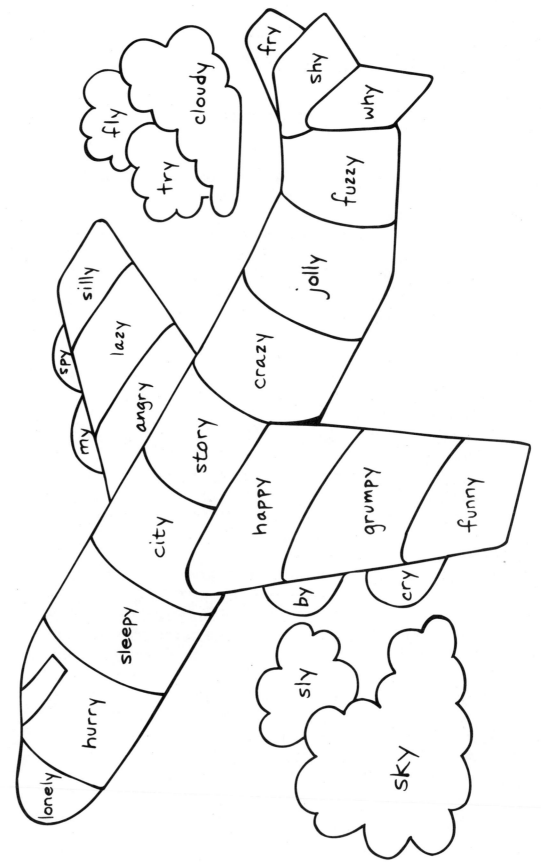

Storybook People

Vocabulary List

dragon	dwarf	elf	fairy
genie	ghost	giant	king
knight	prince	princess	queen
witch	wizard		

Activities:

1. I Wish I Could Be . . . —Daydreams come true as students write about why they would like to be a particular storybook character.
2. Coat of Arms—Students design a personal coat of arms based on medieval concepts.
3. Storybook Land—Imagi-Nation is the place to be as students create a fantasy land to house storybook people.
4. Puppet Plays—This activity integrates script writing, storytelling, and oral communication skills.

Word Study Extension:

The Two Sounds of /g/ Worksheet—A coloring worksheet that lets students practice decoding soft and hard g's.

I Wish I Could Be . . .

Purpose:
Students will use vocabulary words and related concepts in a creative writing project.

Materials:
Writing paper, pencils, variety of reading materials, list of vocabulary words, chalkboard and chalk or overhead projector and marker

Preparation:
Gather a wide selection of reading material, including children's magazines, that is appropriate to your grade level. Find stories that feature characters listed in the vocabulary words.

Procedure:
1. Write the vocabulary words on the chalkboard or overhead projector. Spend some time discussing each word. Tell the students to begin thinking about which of the storybook characters they might like to be. Let the class know that they will have time to make their decision.
2. Show the children the reading materials. Tell the class that you are going to give them some time to read the stories. This will help them get more ideas about the different characters. Allow time for students to read and browse through some of the books. Let them read in corners, in beanbag chairs, under tables, etc. You may wish to have the children do the reading in this session and assign the writing project in a different session.
3. Give the class the following writing assignment: *You are going to write a story about why you would like to be one of the storybook people. Write about all the good things that would happen if you were that character. You should also tell some of the things that might not be so good about being that character. Be sure to tell about where you would live, what you would eat, and how you would spend your time.*
4. Conference with students, and help them edit and correct their work. Provide time for the children to share their stories aloud in class.

Coat of Arms

Purpose:
Students will match symbols to ordinal number concepts in this medieval-art activity.

Materials:
Drawing paper; markers, crayons, or paints; scissors; rulers; information sheet (see p. 117)

Preparation:
1. Make enough copies of the information sheet for each child to have one.
2. Enlarge several of the shield outlines on page 117 for patterns.

Procedure:
1. Give each child an information sheet. Tell the class: *Knights carried shields for protection. Each knight had his own special design painted on his shield. This way, friends would recognize him in battle. The designs were passed down from father to son as a family coat of arms. In a large family, not everyone could carry the exact same design. Sometimes colored borders or extra symbols were added to the family coat of arms. Most of the knights could not read or write, but they were able to find friends and relatives in a crowd by looking at their coat of arms. Many times the designs were also painted on castle walls to show who lived inside. They were used like our street addresses are used today. A coat of arms was also sometimes drawn on important papers.*

    Although each coat of arms was different there were many common patterns. Look at the paper I gave you. Here are some of the patterns that were used. You don't need to learn the names. You will need to pick one of these patterns when you design your own coat of arms. Special symbols were used to tell whether the knight was the first son, second son, and so on. We are going to use these symbols for both sons and daughters. If you are the first child born in your family, you will add the "file" to your design. If you are the fourth child in the family you will add the bird, or "martlet," to your design.

Many times special animals or objects were added to the designs. If a family lived in the forest, they might add a tree to their coat of arms. If the knight lived in a castle with a tall tower, this could be painted on his shield. A lion on his coat of arms meant a knight was strong and brave. A knight might have a dragon on his shield to show that he was a fierce and powerful fighter. A hawk might show that the family was made up of good hunters. A fox could show that the family was smart and clever.

2. Say: *You are going to design your own family coat of arms. Think about things that make your family special. Do you live in a blue house? Then you would want to use a lot of blue in your design. Do you have an animal at home? You could add that to your drawing. Perhaps your family owns a boat. You could draw a boat on your coat of arms. Maybe your last name sounds like the name of an animal or object. This would be a great idea for your design. The knights had to follow all kinds of rules for making their coat of arms. Here are the rules for designing yours:*

> *Choose any of the shield shapes.*
> *Use any of the patterns shown on your information sheet.*
> *Include the mark that shows whether you are the first child, second child, and so on.*
> *Add two or more symbols that tell about you and your family.*

3. Show the children how to trace the shield pattern onto the drawing paper. If you are working with first graders, you may want to cut the shapes out for them ahead of time. Show the children how to use the rulers to help them create the various patterns.

4. Allow several work sessions for the children to complete their designs. Students will be eager to talk about the designs they have created, so provide a sharing time in class.

5. Display the finished coats of arms in the classroom. This is a wonderful display for an Open House or Parent Night.

 Starting Points for Vocabulary © 2000 Monday Morning Books, Inc.

Coat of Arms Patterns and Symbols

Where do you fit in your family?

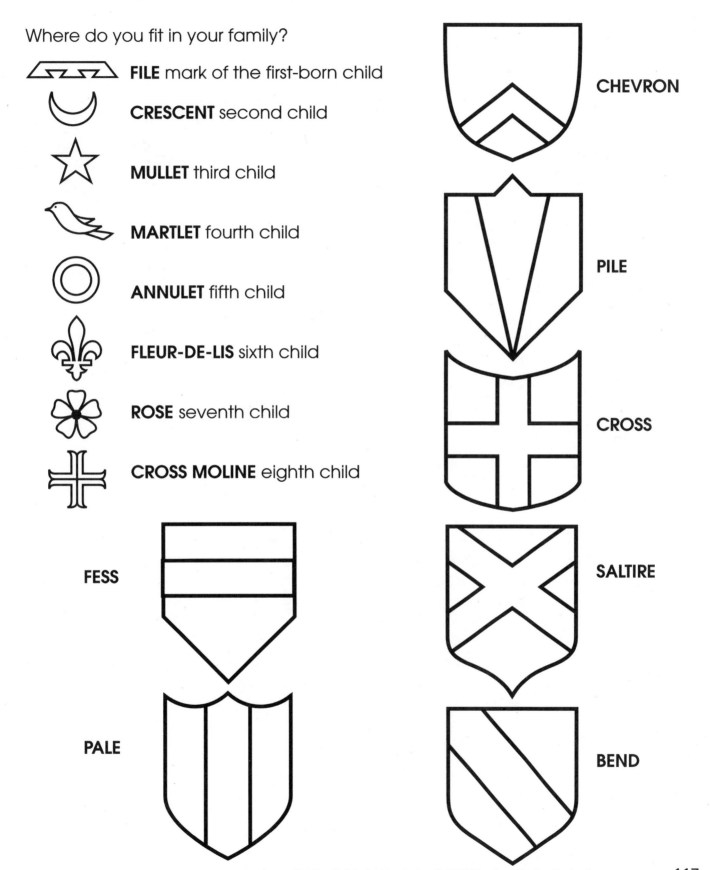

FILE mark of the first-born child

CRESCENT second child

MULLET third child

MARTLET fourth child

ANNULET fifth child

FLEUR-DE-LIS sixth child

ROSE seventh child

CROSS MOLINE eighth child

CHEVRON

PILE

CROSS

FESS

SALTIRE

PALE

BEND

Storybook Land

Purpose:
Students will make a map, capitalize proper nouns, and match vocabulary words to pictures.

Materials:
Drawing paper, markers, crayons, pencils, list of vocabulary words

Preparation:
Students will need to be familiar with the concept of maps. Note: If students have not yet had experience with map skills or proper nouns, the project may be changed to a simple drawing. Ask the children to draw a picture that includes illustrations of as many of the list words as possible. Have them label each person in the drawing with the correct vocabulary word.

Procedure:
1. Ask the children to read one vocabulary word and tell where they think that character might live. Do this with each of the words in the list.
2. Review the concept of maps and labeling if necessary.
3. Tell the students that they are going to create a map of a fantasy land that tells where these characters live. The map should include:

      Homes for at least seven of the storybook people; each of these should be labeled with the correct vocabulary word naming the person who lives inside
      Two roads that have names
      One named body of water (river, lake, ocean, or stream)

Extra points will be given if the storybook people are drawn by their homes.
4. Reinforce the use of proper nouns. Remind students that the names of their roads and body of water will need to begin with capital letters. (See *Starting Points for Grammar*, Monday Morning Books, for more information on teaching this concept.)

Puppet Plays

Purpose:
This multi-faceted activity allows students to practice oral communication and small-group cooperation skills. Students will write scripts and relate vocabulary words to concepts during the process.

Materials:
Writing paper; pencils; list of vocabulary words; reading selection written in play format; art supplies (these will vary depending on the type of puppets you choose to create); sheet, blanket, or tablecloth; table

Preparation:
1. Determine which type of puppet you are going to have the children create for their productions. Paper bag puppets or simple stick puppets work fine. There are many books available that give instructions for making puppets.
2. Find an age-appropriate reading selection in play format. The majority of stories in beginning basal readers are written in this dialogue form.

Procedure:
1. Show the children the play. Point out that in a play, the words a person says have the person's name and a colon in front of them. This tells the reader which person is speaking. Tell the students that this is the way they will write their plays.
2. Divide the class into pairs. Tell each pair to choose two of the storybook people from the vocabulary list. These will be the stars of their play. Children should write a one-page script of dialogue for these two characters. It should be a very simple story, perhaps about a knight who lost his shield, a princess looking for a friend, or a ghost and a dragon who want to play together. Help the children write, edit, and rewrite their scripts.
3. Provide instructions and materials for creating puppets.
4. Drape the blanket over a table to make a puppet stage.
5. Remind the students to use effective oral communication: practice the script, speak loudly and clearly, use expression when they speak. Remind the audience to be quiet and attentive. Enjoy the presentations.

Two Sounds of /g/

Name _____

Color the words with the hard sound of g (as in dragon) green.
Color the words with the soft sound of g (as in giant) orange.

girl
golf
grab
good
grade
gingerbread
general
glow
forget
bridge
bigger
danger
wagon
gentle
magic
guess
large
judge
great
genie
edge
ghost
giant
gym
giggle
garden
strange
gem
giraffe
page
dragon

Homophones

The following pages provide a primary list of homophones. These are words that sound alike but are spelled differently and have totally different meanings. Select those pairs of homophones that are giving your students trouble. You also may wish to choose pairs that you feel would help increase the Puppy Power (see p. 12) of your students' writing. The pairs listed in bold print come from the list of the 500 most frequently used words in children's writing. One or both words from those pairs can be found on the list. Since they use these words often, it is important for children to have a firm understanding of their meaning and master the correct spelling.

Once you have chosen your homophones, use the activities on the following pages. The words you choose may determine which activities you use. For example, "Shape Shifters" (p. 126) works well with hair/hare, pear/pair/pare, eye/I, and boy/buoy. However, it would be a difficult project to do with the words find/fined, moan/mown, and higher/hire. These types of homophones would best be practiced through an activity such as "Memory Game" (p. 124).

Since homophones sound alike, using the words orally does nothing to help students master their differences. Provide plenty of opportunities for students to use the words in written form.

Activities:
1. Memory Game—The childhood classic lets children match homophone pairs.
2. Partner Pair-ups—A party-style game that involves matching homophones and writing sentences.
3. Shape Shifters—An art project that enhances visualization of word meaning.
4. Butterfly Mobiles—This craft classic helps students match up homophone pairs.

Homophone List

A
acts, ax
air, heir
aisle, I'll, isle
allowed, aloud
ant, aunt
ate, eight

B
bail, bale
ball, bawl
bare, bear
be, bee
been, bin
berry, bury
birth, berth
board, bored
bow, bough
boy, buoy
by, bye, buy

C
capital, capitol
ceiling, sealing
cell, sell
cent, scent, sent
chord, cord, cored
chute, shoot
close, clothes
coarse, course
creak, creek

D
days, daze
dear, deer
dense, dents
dew, do, due
die, dye
doe, dough

E
earn, urn
eye, I
eyed, I'd

F
find, fined
fir, fur
flea, flee
flour, flower
for, fore, four

G
grate, great
groan, grown
guessed, guest

H
hair, hare
heal, heel
hear, here
heard, herd
higher, hire
him, hymn
hoarse, horse
hole, whole
hour, our

K
knead, need
knew, new
knight, night
knot, not
know, no
knows, nose

L
lead, led
loan, lone

M
made, maid
mail, male
main, mane
might, mite
miner, minor
moan, mown

N
none, nun

O
oar, or, ore
one, won

P
pail, pale
pain, pane
pair, pare, pear
pause, paws
peace, piece
peak, peek
peal, peel
peer, pier
plain, plane
pleas, please
praise, prays, preys
prince, prints
principal, principle

R
rain, reign, rein
raise, rays
rap, wrap
read, red
read, reed
real, reel
right, write
ring, wring
road, rode, rowed
rose, rows

S
sail, sale
scene, seen
sea, see
sew, so, sow
side, sighed
sighs, size

soar, sore
soared, sword
sole, soul
some, sum
son, sun
stairs, stares
stake, steak
steal, steel

T
tacks, tax
tail, tale
tear, tier
tense, tents
their, there, they're
threw, through
throne, thrown
to, too, two
toad, toed, towed

V
vain, vane, vein

W
wail, whale
waist, waste
wait, weight
ware, wear, where
way, weigh, whey
weak, week
weather, whether
which, witch
wood, would

Y
your, you're

Memory Game

Purpose:
In this classic game, students use visual memory and concentration skills to match homophone pairs.

Materials:
Index cards (20 cards for each group of students), markers, scissors, list of homophones

Preparation:
1. Cut the index cards in half.
2. Using a marker, write one homophone on one half of each card and the matching homophone on the other half. You may wish to use a different color for each matching set to aid young students.

Procedure:
1. Divide the class into groups of two to four players. (If you are not planning to have the whole class participate, use a learning center concept. Place the cards and instructions in an area where a group of students may play the game.) Tell the students that the object of the game is to make the most correct matches of pairs of homophones.
2. Shuffle the cards and lay them out on a table face down in columns and rows. Once the cards have been placed, they should not be moved around.
3. The first player turns over two cards. If the cards match (form a pair of homophones), the player keeps them and takes another turn.
4. If the cards do not match, they are returned to their original positions and play moves to the next person.
5. Play continues until all the cards have been correctly matched. The person with the most cards is the winner.

Starting Points for Vocabulary © 2000 Monday Morning Books, Inc.

Partner Pair-ups

Purpose:
This game requires students to use oral communication skills to solve a problem. Students also write vocabulary words in complete sentences.

Materials:
Scraps of colored paper, markers, masking tape, paper, pencils, scissors

Preparation:
Cut the scraps of paper into small squares. Divide the squares into sets of two. Choose pairs of homophones. Write one homophone on each square. If you have an odd number of students in your class, include one triple homophone set, such as there, their, they're or to, too, two.

Procedure:
1. Shuffle the word squares you have prepared. Use the masking tape to tape one word to the back of each child.
2. Tell the children that they must first find out which word they have on their back. They must do this by politely asking someone to read the word to them. Next, they must find the person with the matching homophone. This may be determined by searching backs or by getting information from other students. A student might ask, "Did you see anyone with the word 'merry'?"
3. Once students have paired up, they may remove the homophones from their backs. They should then write each homophone in two different sentences for a total of four sentences. (If you have a group of three students you will need to decide how many sentences they are to complete.)

Shape Shifters

Purpose:
Students will create visual clues to illustrate word meanings.

Materials:
Drawing paper; crayons, colored pencils, or markers; list of homophones

Preparation:
Write the list of desired homophones on the board. Here are some recommended pairs that work well for this activity:

ant, aunt	boy, buoy	close, clothes	eye, I
fir, fur	flour, flower	hair, hare	knight, night
mail, male	pail, pale	pair, pare	peace, piece
peak, peek	prince, prints	rain, rein	road, rode
sail, sale	son, sun	stake, steak	tail, tale

Procedure:
1. Ask the students to choose a set of homophones. Ask them to see what picture comes to mind for each word. For example, "close" might bring up a picture of a closed door; "clothes" might make them see a shirt or dress.
2. Tell the students to think of a simple shape or outline that can represent each word. Have them use crayons or markers to draw an outline of each shape. Then have students print each corresponding word several times inside the shape. Tell students that they may write the words so that they follow the contours of the shapes if they wish.
3. Have students complete at least five sets of words in this manner.

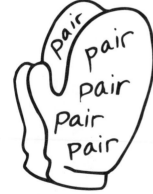

Starting Points for Vocabulary © 2000 Monday Morning Books, Inc.

Butterfly Mobiles

Purpose:
Students match homophone pairs in this art project.

Materials:
Colored paper, wire hangers, scissors, hole punch, string, butterfly pattern (see next page), markers, list of homophones, chalkboard and chalk

Preparation:
1. Cut the colored paper into rectangles 4" x 8" (10 cm x 20 cm).
2. Collect wire coat hangers. These may be obtained from cleaners, garage sales, or from a request to parents and colleagues. Remove any paper or cardboard that may be attached to the hangers.
3. Make copies of the butterfly pattern so that each child may have one.

Procedure:
1. Tell the children that a mobile is an art form that uses hanging images to show movement. Tell the class that they are going to create mobiles using the images of butterflies. Draw a butterfly on the board. Point out its two wings. Tell the class that whatever design is on one wing of the butterfly is also found on the other wing. The designs on butterflies come in pairs. Tell the students that they are going to decorate their butterflies with pairs of homophones.
2. Give each child five pieces of colored paper. Help students fold the paper in half so that they have a square that is 4" x 4" (10 cm x 10 cm). Show the children how to carefully lay the pattern on the fold of the square. Instruct the students to slowly draw around the outside of the pattern. Once the outline has been drawn, students should cut along this line. Remind students that they should not cut along the fold of the paper.

3. Have students unfold each butterfly they have created. Remind them that the designs on the butterfly are the same on each wing. You may wish to discuss the terms symmetry and symmetrical. Tell the students that the designs on these butterflies are going to be written in words. The words will be pairs of homophones. For example, if they write "bear" on the right wing they must write "bare" in the same location on the left wing. Tell the students to decorate the front and back of the butterflies since both sides will be visible. Require that at least six pairs of homophones be written on each butterfly.

4. When the butterflies have been decorated, punch a hole in the top of each one. Tie varying lengths of string to the butterflies and tie the strings to hangers to display.

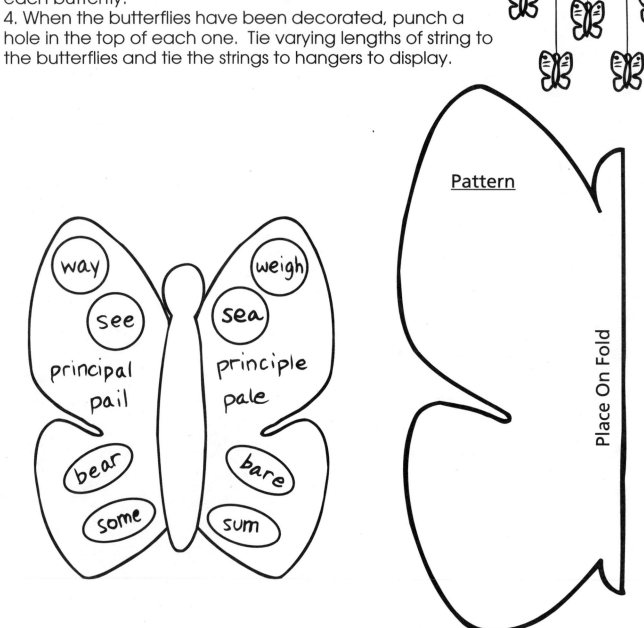

Pattern

Place On Fold

Starting Points for Vocabulary © 2000 Monday Morning Books, Inc.